TOPIC WORK IN THE PRIMARY SCHOOL

TOPIC WORK IN THE PRIMARY SCHOOL

TREVOR KERRY and JIM EGGLESTON

ROUTLEDGE
London

First published in 1988 by
Routledge
a division of Routledge, Chapman and Hall
11 New Fetter Lane, London EC4P 4EE

Filmset by Mayhew Typesetting, Bristol, England
Printed and bound in Great Britain by
Biddles Ltd, Guildford and King's Lynn

British Library Cataloguing in Publication Data

Kerry, Trevor
   Topic work in the primary school.
   1. Elementary school teaching — Great
  Britain. 2. Education, Elementary —
  Great Britain — Curricula
  I. Title II. Eggleston, J.F. (James
  Frederick)
  372.13′0941   LB1564.G7
  ISBN 0-415-00548-5
      0-415-00549-3 pbk

Contents

Figures

Tables

The Authors

TREVOR KERRY graduated in the University of Durham and taught in schools in the London Borough of Havering. After eight years at Bishop Grosseteste College he became co-ordinator of the DES Teacher Education Project at Nottingham University, producing training materials for initial and in-service training. Following a brief spell at Charlotte Mason College he returned to Nottingham as co-ordinator of the Schools Council project described in this book. Since then he has been Head of the Department of Applied Social Sciences at Doncaster Metropolitan Institute of Higher Education and Principal's Representative for the Mexborough campus. He is contributing editor of the Macmillan series *Focus* and *Focus on education*, has written *Invitation to teaching* and *Teaching infants* (with Janice Tollitt) for Basil Blackwell, and edited *Finding and helping the able child* and *Mixed ability teaching* (with Margaret Sands) for Croom Helm. He obtained his PhD in Education in 1982.

JIM EGGLESTON graduated in zoology at Durham University and, following a spell in the Army, taught in schools in Leicestershire. From there he joined the University of Leicester, and specialised in the analysis of transactions between teachers and pupils in science lessons. The result was the Science Teacher Observation Schedule (STOS); and the findings from this work were published by Macmillan. He was appointed Professor of Education at Nottingham University in 1973, and headed the higher degrees and PGCE divisions of the School of Education. He was Director, with Howard Bradley, of the Schools Council project reported in this book. He has acted as consultant to a substantial number of educational projects and institutions at home and overseas. His previous publications include *A critical review of assessment procedures in secondary school science* (Research Unit for Assessment and Curriculum Studies, University of Leicester, 1965) and *Studies in assessment* (with J.F. Kerr, English Universities Press, London, 1968).

Acknowledgements

Our thanks are due to Linda Wightman, who typed the original version of this manuscript; and to Sheila Reilly, who coped with the amendments and revisions.

This work was carried out with the help of the Schools Council Programme Two grant for the project 'Developing pupils' thinking through topic work'. The authors wish to express their thanks to the School Curriculum Development Committee, which superseded the Schools Council, for releasing the copyright of this material to them.

Our gratitude is due, too, to all those LEA officers, head teachers and teachers who allowed us access to their classrooms, and to those who gave very freely of their time and energy to collect data for us. It would be impossible to name all the participants across the seven LEAs involved; but a number assisted beyond the call of duty. Among these were Brian Perry, Joan Robbins, Peter Cast, Pat Partington and Stan Hall. The work of our honorary research assistant, Annette Bancroft (née Miles), was also much appreciated.

To preserve confidentiality, names of head teachers, teachers, pupils, schools and locations have been altered throughout the text. This in no way detracts from our debt to all those who participated.

We wish to thank those who have given us permission to include extracts from their work which were not part of case studies. Peter Cast agreed to reproduction of sections of his handbook 'All the Years Round'; the headteachers and Mrs Thompson allowed quotation from staff handbooks of Asterdale primary school and of Boston Tower Road primary school. If we have inadvertently failed to acknowledge other sources we invite notification and we apologise in advance.

Finally, a special word of thanks must go to Carolle Kerry, who worked through the proofs with meticulous care, though we acknowledge responsibility for any errors that have crept through to the final production.

To our former colleagues in the School of Education at Nottingham University, with whom we shared many happy hours.

Preface

This is a book about topic work in the primary school. It resulted from a former Schools Council project, 'Developing pupils' thinking through topic work' (1981–3), run jointly at the University of Nottingham and the Cambridge Institute of Education.

The major purpose of the book is to explore and set out some findings from the case studies which formed the research-based underpinning of this curriculum development project. We believe that in doing this we shall be meeting the needs of five audiences.

The book will be useful to teachers in primary and middle schools because it looks at a common method of working — the topic — and uses the collective professional wisdom of other teachers to illuminate problems and practices. The text is not a prescription but a prompt to start practitioners thinking about their own classroom practice.

We believe the book will be of interest to educational researchers because it tries to exemplify ways in which case-study material, sensitively used and appropriately analysed, can illuminate teachers' skills. Applied research is not only topical, it is essential if educational research is to have meaning.

Head teachers should find much of interest here. Over and over again in our case histories of topics we were thrown back to ask questions about the management structures of schools. Some were effective, others less so. But the management of learning, though less pressing than the management of resources, is at least as crucial. It is an area where an increased debate would be opportune.

Educational administrators might well take heed of what is reported here. With an increasing awareness of accountability it is becoming more and more urgent to describe effective practice in teaching. This book contributes a little to that end.

Finally, student teachers in training will find much sound advice, and perhaps some salutary warnings, arising out of the cases described. This is a book that might well form part of a prescribed reading list for the primary trainee.

With these purposes and audiences in mind, a word about the layout of the book is in order. The Introduction describes the Schools Council Project, its collection of case-study data, and looks at case study as a research technique. Chapter 1 is substantial. It is intended to be in part a review of the relevant literature and in part a glance at historical practice; in brief, it is a description of the 'state of the art' of topic teaching and the rationale which underpins it.

The rest of the book, except for the Conclusion, discusses aspects of case studies of topic work in action. Chapter 2 looks at topic work in action from the points of view of the head teacher, the class teacher and a researcher in the same school. It shows how a close scrutiny of classroom practice can be used to begin to cull out questions about one's own (and other people's) classroom performance.

Chapter 3 discusses issues which arise from the case studies. The chapter forms an overview of the research carried out by the case-study team, and the major areas of question raised by the case studies about the ways in which teachers handle topic work in primary schools. These individual issues are then dealt with in subsequent chapters.

Chapter 4 is concerned with the management of the curriculum. The case-study material is used to generate thought about issues in managing the curriculum both at school level and at the classroom level. These case studies illustrate the life of a real school, and lead the reader on to look at his or her own institution in the light of the issues raised. Chapter 5 deals with preparation for topic work. The chapter looks at the natural history of the topic: how it begins, how the teacher handles it in the classroom, and how it ends. This section of the book concentrates specifically on the methods of planning and their respective merits; and analyses for example what teachers mean when they employ flow charts and how they can utilise this kind of planning activity more effectively.

In chapter 6 we move on to classroom processes. In the first of two chapters on classroom processes we look at the teaching context. Here we explore in some detail what goes on in classrooms so that we can analyse the teacher's performance as, for example, a questioner, a manager and an explainer. The collective application of these insights to what goes on in the lesson is shown to be a way in which teachers can improve their own performance through self-analysis. In the second chapter on classroom processes, chapter 7, we look at teaching skills and professional development. This chapter puts the spotlight on the skills which a teacher needs to tackle a topic-work lesson. A detailed case study of a lesson in progress is analysed piece by piece to show the strengths and weaknesses of the teacher at work. The chapter is very positive in nature, and from it the reader will be able to come to terms with looking at his or her own performance in the classroom.

We move in chapters 8 and 9 to evaluating learning. These

chapters take a close look at how learning is evaluated, for example through record-keeping systems; and also consider questions of how learning can be more effectively evaluated, for example by scrutinising what concepts, skills or information the teacher needs to impart to pupils, and how the teacher measures whether he or she has been successful.

In the Conclusion to the book we stand back from the individual cases and try to gain an overview of the messages gleaned from teachers and head teachers and from the literature about what constitutes successful topic work. In a very real sense we shall be looking here at what constitutes successful *teaching*, whether or not it is carried out within the context of studying a topic, project or theme. To this extent the book has validity for all primary teachers who wish to improve their professional self-confidence. The message of the book is one of professional self-development through self-scrutiny, and the sharing of professional insights with fellow teachers.

An appendix to the book offers some practical suggestions about resources for topic work, both printed and audio-visual. It has to be emphasised however that the key actor in the drama of teaching is the teacher, in his or her interaction with the pupils. Good-quality materials are a positive help in providing a suitable and stimulating educational environment, but ultimately we are concerned with the quality of the teaching and learning process as exemplified in the cases on which this book is based.

Introduction

Case Studies in Topic Work

The Schools Council Project

This book is a description of just part of the Schools Council project 'Developing pupils' thinking through topic work'. The project came into being in 1981 as a result of a grant from the Council's Programme Two. It was directed by Professor Jim Eggleston and Howard Bradley, co-ordinated by Dr Trevor Kerry, and located at Nottingham University and the Cambridge Institute of Education. The project had a two-year life-span, during which its terms of reference were to explore children's thinking during topic-work lessons and to design training materials for the in-service education of teachers. The former task, part of the findings from which form the substance of this book, informed the latter. The in-service materials were published by the School Curriculum Development Committee and Longman in 1985. This book looks at sections of the case-study material generated by the project, with a view to examining in more detail some of the practice of topic teaching and to raising what to us seem to be critical issues in thinking through effective teaching in topic lessons. Before we can proceed to set out the case-study extracts, however, it is necessary to do three things. Firstly, we shall look briefly at how the project team collected its data. Secondly, since many of these were in case-study form, we shall consider the value of this type of data for throwing light on the practice of teaching. Both of these concerns will be dealt with in this Introduction. Thirdly, in chapter 1, there will be an attempt to analyse the evolution of topic work into its present form through a use of some of the project's own data but also by reference to the wider literature of the subject.

THE PROJECT'S RESEARCH

The Schools Council project was a research and development project of relatively short duration. If its fundamental purpose was to be achieved, that is, the generation of in-service training materials based upon surveys of current practice, then the research element had to be completed quite quickly: certainly within twelve months. The research was, therefore, divided into phases.

Phase 1

This was initiated extremely rapidly. It consisted of a questionnaire, semi-structured but very detailed. It was devised in two versions, one for teachers and one for head teachers. The questionnaire was mailed to heads and staff in a stratified random sample of 63 schools in the East Midlands. The scope of the questionnaire was to cover what appeared from the literature and in the view of a group of experienced educators to be key areas of concern: the management of learning at school and classroom level; preparation for topic teaching; aims and intentions; specific lesson procedures and problems; methods of evaluation; and the criteria for success in topic work for both teachers and pupils. There was space for the respondents to make spontaneous freehand comments about the questionnaire. To complete the questionnaire took most respondents about an hour. In the event this quite demanding questionnaire was completed by 25 per cent of potential respondents spread over 61 per cent of the contact schools. Its main purpose within the context of the project was to highlight major areas of concern which could be explored in a deeper way through subsequent case study in a smaller sample of schools. The findings from this exercise are noted from time to time in this book, particularly in chapter 1, and the item itself is referred to for convenience as the Phase 1 Questionnaire.

Phase 2

The second phase consisted of drawing out the insights from the questionnaire in order to initiate very detailed case studies of individual schools selected by the advisory service in three East Midlands counties. Eight university tutors and advisers participated in the data collection, which included written accounts of regular visits to the study schools to see topics taught through from beginning to end. In addition heads and teachers both filled in Phase 1 Questionnaires and were interviewed on tape. Case-study workers also collected samples of pupils' work, discussed the children's work with them, recorded children on tape, collected evidence in the form of staff handbooks, and carried out systematic observations using prepared schedules (for example to analyse questions or to measure pupils' time on task). The case-study workers were expected to use initiative and professional judgement to gather whatever data appeared to be useful and relevant. They were briefed before embarking on the exercise, and met intermittently with the co-ordinator and with each other to compare notes. The result was a substantial bank of data in various media. These case studies form the bulk of the material extracted in this book to illustrate the issues which were highlighted by the research and which are discussed in chapters 2–8.

Phase 3

The third research phase was conducted simultaneously with Phase 2, that is, in the period February–June 1981, following the leads provided by the Phase 1 Questionnaire, which was administered in November 1980–January 1981. Phase 3 consisted of identifying a number of interested schools and teachers with the help of LEA advisers, and of gaining the agreement of teachers to invest a substantial amount of time in keeping records of themselves at work in preparing and executing topics. These records were called Self-Report Case Studies. The Self-Report Case Studies are also extracted in later chapters of this book alongside material collected by observers in Phase 2. The arguments for the validity of self-reporting are taken up later in this Introduction.

The Schools Council Project, then, involved three interrelated phases of research. The research identified questions or issues about the practice of topic work in primary schools. This book goes on to identify the issues and to illustrate them from the two kinds of case study described here: observer-generated and self-report. But first it is opportune to consider the validity and importance of case study as a means of investigating teaching method.

CASE STUDY AS A RESEARCH METHOD

Case study has its roots in anthropology and sociology, and has but recently come into its own in educational research. It stands at the open-minded or ethnomethodological end of the continuum 'open-minded — pre-ordained' (Wragg and Kerry 1978). Its advantages are argued as being qualitative rather than quantitative (Stake and Day 1978, House 1980). Put at its most basic, it consists of an observer sitting in on a situation and describing as accurately and objectively as possible precisely what occurs. This view of case study is technically labelled 'scientific phenomenology' and 'contributes a strong and concerted effort to avoid, or at least significantly minimize, interpretation (bias) by the observer' (Kenny and Grotelveschen 1984). But human beings, even case-study workers, do have biases, interpretations, preconceptions: so it is argued that a 'philosophical phenomenology' is acceptable, that is, one which allows for these presuppositions in viewing the data collected (A. Schutz, in Luckmann 1978).

Given that case studies are detailed records of events, collected faithfully, but by observers who may bias the recording by his or her preconceptions, the traditional debate has been between those who favour this open or qualitative approach and those who seek more objective quantitative measures. But the two approaches are not so mutually exclusive as some advocates would claim. Common sense suggests that some aspects of behaviour (how many times a pupil yawns during a lesson) may be more amenable to quantification than others (the evidence for interest in a topic). There may (or may not) be interrelationships between the two phenomena, but these could be indirect or subtle (a late night, the teacher's failure to open a window, recurrent lethargy after glandular fever). Thus in the case studies reported in this book the case-study worker exercised judgement in moving from open modes of reporting to more structured ones as he or she felt appropriate to the particular situation.

Case study itself now has a respectable pedigree in educational research methodology, and the ground rules for its execution are well documented (Nisbet and Watt 1978). Knight (1985), for instance, found fifty examples of case studies in school-based curriculum development alone documented in theses and journals between 1973 and 1983. Atkins (1984) concluded that 'a rigid distinction between the quantitative and qualitative approaches is conceptually unsound' since neither is value-free, but he notes the different emphases of the two traditions:

PRACTITIONER AS RESEARCHER

TABLE 1 FOCUS ON METHODS

QUANTITATIVE FOCUS ON	*QUALITATIVE FOCUS ON*
Study and explanation of manifest behaviour	Discovery and understanding of personal meaning
Search for 'laws' governing human behaviour; deterministic	Illumination of intersubjective construction of reality
Claim for objective truth	Claim for relative truths
Prediction on basis of statistical generalisability	General held to be inherent in particular. Reliance on informed judgment of reader to assess generalisation to other known contexts
Repeated patterns, trends and central tendencies in phenomena	Relationships and distinctions between cases. The unique an acceptable subject of research
Outcomes, results and products	Processes
Natural science paradigms	Arts paradigms
Measurement and testing instruments to collect data	Researcher as own instrument in collection of evidence
Detachment of researcher	Involvement/participation of researcher

At all events, the ability to establish quantitative data from qualitative case-study data in a practical teaching context (in the form of protocols, i.e. lesson accounts) was pioneered in the California beginning teacher evaluation study (Berliner and Tikunoff 1976), and has been replicated many times since both in the USA and in Britain.

So in using case-study data, particularly when such data were supported by excursions into the quantitative through semi-structured questionnaires and systematic observation, the Schools Council project found itself in good company methodologically. Atkins is right to draw attention to the fact that it is the reader himself who must bring his or her own element of interpretation to bear in judging the particular significance of the data, and this you will have the opportunity to do in chapters 2–8 of the book. Meanwhile, however, the next task is to pick up a point from Atkins's table where he refers to the researcher as his own instrument in the collection of evidence. Phase 3 of our research used what we described as self-report case studies, and it is to these we must turn attention briefly.

THE SELF-REPORT CASE STUDIES

Though the methods and procedures of case-study research are well documented, those of self-reporting are not. The following paragraphs are designed to describe and justify this method for collecting data. They were originally written as part of a contribution to the *Westminster Studies in Education* journal (Kerry 1984).

Setting up the self-report case studies

Few teachers, except those most recently emerged from BEd Honours courses, have been taught to think in research terms. Therefore, the setting up of a self-report system of case studies had to be meticulously planned. The first step was to try to put together a self-report package, a guideline document, which would give the respondents a framework within which to record their activities sensitively and in detail. It had to be probing, with a structure shared by all respondents, but flexible enough to allow for individual initiatives in recording unique classroom events. It had, too, to solicit information about the key areas highlighted by the original questionnaire as in need of exploration and included in those case studies conducted by trained observers. Inevitably, the package would look sizeable, but an eye would be kept on length so that it did not discourage too many potential users. The final research package consisted of four parts, which are described in the following paragraphs.

1. The first part of the self-report case study asked teachers to complete a questionnaire, in fact the identical questionnaire which had been used in the first research phase. There were several good reasons for this. The questionnaire was known to explore thoroughly and economically a teacher's basic attitudes to, and procedures within, topic lessons. There was already a pool of existing information resulting from the use of the questionnaire and so the data from the self-reports could be compared with this as a way of seeing the self-report respondent's position within a wider scheme of topic-work teaching, and to determine what was 'typical' and what was

'distinctive' about the teacher in question. The feeling was also that this was a stock-taking exercise for the teacher, a kind of self-analysis which was open-ended enough not to distort his or her thinking, but stimulating enough to get the respondent into an appropriate frame of mind for self-reporting.

2. If part one served as a background to the teacher's topic work in general, then part two of the self-report package concentrated on the specific topic to be taught and reported upon by the respondent. Christened the Topic Outline Proforma, it asked for the topic title, an outline of the content (including flow diagrams, examples of worksheets), and the resources available. Then it went on to explore the progress the teacher intended the pupils to make during the topic socially and in terms of knowledge gained, skills practised and attitudes to learning or subject matter. Questions were included about provisions for the most and least able, the planned duration of the topic, its links with other curriculum areas, and the processes for monitoring and assessing pupils' progress. Two final questions looked at the teacher's expected outcomes of the project, and the roles he or she expected to play.

The first two parts of the self-report package could be completed before any classroom teaching took place. The questionnaire could be timed well in advance of the lessons covered by the self-report activity, and the Topic Outline Proforma could be absorbed with a minimum of effort into the teacher's standard preparation procedures. In these ways, the workload was spread and interference minimised. Parts three and four, however, needed attention during the period of the teaching of the topic itself.

3. Part three was designed as a diary sheet to record the events of a lesson. Respondents were not asked to complete a diary sheet for every topic lesson taught, but for one such lesson per week for the topic's duration. The diary sheet was seen as central to the whole affair, since it would replace the case-study worker's lesson notes of the main case-study sample. It asked for responses to these questions or instructions:

(a) What were your intentions, aims or objectives for this lesson?
(b) Describe briefly your lesson organisation for the session (use of space, or of whole-class or individualised learning, etc).
(c) What particular *teaching strategies* were used, e.g. problem-solving, class discussion?

(d) What task or tasks were the pupils set?

(e) By the end of the lesson what new information, skills and concepts had the pupils acquired?

(f) Looking back, with what aspects of the lesson were you most and least satisfied?

(g) Please include worksheets, etc., as examples of work done.

(h) Add any comments of your own.

Teachers had to spend a good deal of time on this, but it was crucial to the whole operation.

4. The fourth part of the self-analysis document was a weekly summary sheet which asked the teachers to look back over the week and to record anything which had affected their own planning of the pupils' learning. Specific questions probed the learning difficulties of individual pupils, resource production and management, and things to be borne in mind when planning the next week's work.

The complete package as it came to the teachers in the self-report group, then, contained a questionnaire, a topic outline proforma, six diary sheets to record six individual lessons, and six weekly summary sheets. The case study was to extend over a six-week period or up to half a term if the topic lasted that long. In addition, the document was equipped with clear but detailed instructions for use. Though sizeable, half of it could be completed and put aside before the classroom teaching began. In the event, 11 teachers out of 21 (52 per cent) invited to take part did so. The next question was whether their self-reporting would be adequate for our purposes.

Some criteria for judging success

Adelman *et al*. (1977) remarked that 'case study is an umbrella term for a family of research methods having in common the decision to focus an enquiry round an instance'. Nisbet and Watt (1978) add:

the method attempts to give a fair and accurate account of a specific case in such a way as to allow the reader to penetrate the superficial record, and also to check the author's interpretations by examining an appropriate selection of objective evidence from which the case study has been built.

Our self-report case studies differed from most in a significant way. While most case studies are compiled by an observer-researcher and written up by him for an audience, ours were to be compiled by the teacher-subject and given to the researchers as fodder for in-service materials. By definition, the role of the subject as researcher would call into question the objectivity of these cases. While they did not need to satisfy the ultimate canons of objective research — they were to augment other more conventional case studies and to do so in a curriculum developmental, rather than in a purely research, role — nevertheless, some degree of objectivity was required to inform professional practice.

To judge the worth of these case studies, then, this objectivity needed to be scrutinised. In effect, the project researchers needed to answer a number of questions about these self-report studies:

(a) Were they detailed enough both to be an accurate portrayal of the topic work being examined and to be valuable as potential development material for use in curriculum initiatives for the in-service training of other teachers?

(b) Were they sensitive enough to be a realistic and credible account of what happened in the topic-work lessons described?

(c) Was there evidence of self-analysis by the teachers in their self-reporting?

(d) Were the accounts honest?

(e) Would actual use of extracts from these self-report cases be of value in the in-service role at the evaluation stage?

If the answers to the foregoing questions were satisfactory, then it would appear that this could well be a useful methodology for similar research and development projects which needed to increase sample sizes at the research stage against a background of limited manpower.

Satisfying the criteria for success in self-reporting

Perhaps the best way to assess the effectiveness of the self-report case studies is to illustrate or comment upon how they satisfied each of the criteria verbalised in the foregoing questions.

As regards detailed and accurate portrayal of classroom life, the respondents went to considerable lengths to supply even minute details. In one case study the teacher augmented his written returns with a tape of a concert of American music which resulted from the topic on the United States. Not content with this, he felt that he should also include a tape of the rehearsal for the concert, since so many teaching points were made in it. A second teacher, who had pursued the theme 'Castles', had turned the classroom (inside and outside) into a castle: the door had a portcullis attached, lights were turned into chandeliers, windows had mock bars across them. All this he documented on colour-slide and added a suitable commentary. Here were ready-made results from topic-work lessons, described and commented upon by their chroniclers, and ready for use by other teachers as stimulus materials.

The written accounts were often sensitive too, and sensitive enough to make them credible. A short quotation from the diary sheet illustrates the judgement. The teacher is writing about a topic on a favourite theme, 'How we used to live 1936–1953':

The aim of this [first] lesson was to introduce the children to the topic. I aimed to stimulate their interest for the forthcoming television series around which our topic will develop. I intended to give the class a broad introduction to the period to be studied and suggested ways in which they might be able to make personal contributions. This was a class lesson based on a discussion introduced by me. The second part of the lesson involved the children compiling individual questionnaires to be taken home later and discussed with grandparents or older relatives. The class discussion centred mainly around a question and answer technique, with the pupils contributing any previous knowledge.

After an initial explanation of how to compile a questionnaire, each child composed a list of questions that they would ask a grandparent about life in 1936. These were then marked before the children took home a neatly written, corrected copy of the questionnaire.

By the end of the lesson I wanted the pupils to have set the topic period into a time-scale they could relate to. The class discussion required skills; and while most of the pupils had these some pupils transferred recently from the remedial unit did not, and had to begin to learn these. The exercise of posing questions made the pupils think, and careful thought was needed to make sure they were phrased in such a way that the children could compare life in the 1980s with 1936.

I was satisfied that the children showed great enthusiasm for the topic and are looking forward to meeting the Hodgkins family on the TV series. They were also keen to discuss the school work with their relatives.

Copies of the pupils' questionnaires are attached [i.e. to the original self-report account]. On reflection, in future I would review ways to correlate this information and compare the pupils' results more effectively.

Such an account seems to satisfy all the criteria reviewed so far: detail, accuracy, realism and credibility. It begins, towards the end, to satisfy that of self-analysis, too. Other accounts exemplify this last criterion. A topic on 'Owls' was progressing satisfactorily in a small rural primary school on an isolated fen. The teacher completed a series of weekly diary sheets as things progressed, and here is an extract from one of them:

It is obvious that some children are working at a much slower pace than others, but rather than having half-finished pieces of work I have been giving these slow ones more time. Some children, mostly in order to catch up a bit, are not thinking for themselves but are copying ideas from the more able. This insistence on finishing work might be a distinct disadvantage, making the project drag out; but at least the slow pupils are producing and finishing work — eventually; and this is giving them satisfaction. My problem now is finding work matched to individual abilities and this I must bear in mind in next week's planning . . .

This extract is certainly self-analytical; and it seems honest. Even more honest, perhaps, was the way teachers were prepared to record things which were demonstrably less than perfect:

Due to the start of the World Cup and rehearsals for the school play — both of which are incorporated into the children's curriculum work — the topic has now been curtailed . . . some parts that were planned will not now be dealt with.

This pragmatism was characteristic of the accounts, and it is perhaps an additional measure of their authenticity that they include the highlights and the shadows, the successes and the warts, of classroom reality.

Cross-checking the data

Having established, however, that teachers were prepared to keep sustained records of their own classroom activities, that they could remain faithful to a research proforma in so doing, and that the

11

resulting reports satisfied the criteria of success indicated in the previous section, it was still felt to be important to cross-check the data for validity. If the self-report case studies were to be proved valid then they could be used in two ways: to augment the research reports of the project and to help compile in-service training materials based on real classroom events. To this end the project personnel maintained a programme of informal visits to the classrooms of participating teachers and recorded impressions and incidents they witnessed to compare with the teachers' own accounts. Two examples of this cross-checking process may suffice to illustrate its nature.

At Wheeldon School the class teacher of year three was tackling a topic on 'Castles'. The project observer visited the school four times during this topic. On each occasion a description of the events taking place in the classroom was compiled, either in note form or on tape. These observations were then compared with the teacher's completed proforma. In addition, colour-slides of the pupils' work were produced: hard evidence that the resulting display work described by the teacher and seen by the observer actually existed and that the classroom genuinely had been transformed into another era! Placed side by side, the teacher's account and the observer's impressions allowed a comparison of perspective under the various headings of the self-report proforma list on page 9 (a)–(e).

The observer made three visits to Hamlets JMI, the location of the 'Owls' topic described above. He specifically noted the pupils' emerging written work in the class, their dissection and display of the contents of owl pellets, and the fact that the pupils showed a considerable range of achievement, which meant that — after the passage of some weeks — they were becoming widely separated in both quantity and quality of the tasks set. He also picked up the problems of diminishing available time to complete the topic that were noted by the teaching head himself in the extract quoted in the previous section; though the observer felt that an additional significant factor in this was the presence of the telephone in the ever-open office adjoining the classroom — a phenomenon perhaps too familiar to the head himself to seem worthy of record.

The observer was also able to *add* data to the self-report studies by including descriptions of school facilities, the local environment, and his impressions of school ethos gained, for example, over a school lunch or during break in the staffroom.

Evidence from these observer visits suggested that what the teachers *did* record was substantially accurate in all cases. In just one instance the observer felt that there was an important omission, notably that the pupils were consistently uninterested in the work in progress: a phenomenon not mentioned by the teacher's self-report. It was possible in this instance to triangulate the data by placing a second, un-primed observer into this class; and wholly independently she made a similar comment about disaffection.

Overall, then, these self-report studies seemed both to satisfy the criteria of success which the project team required as a pre-condition for using them as research material, and also to be substantially corroborated by independent observation. It was concluded, therefore, that, once teachers had become used to conforming to the guidelines supplied, these self-report case studies were no more liable to a charge of bias than any other form of ethnographic reporting. In our case the monitoring of each case by an independent observer considerably strengthened the value of the data.

The participants' viewpoint

It was not possible logistically to talk in depth to every teacher who completed a self-report case-study package. But it was possible to chat informally with some and to interview others more formally. In these ways the project team was able to gain some impression of whether the teachers found the exercise valuable.

Two points were universal: it was time-consuming, but the effort expended had been worth while because it had forced the participant to think more carefully about his or her own practice. In effect, then, involvement even at the research level had in-service implications.

A number of other points were made, among them that the rather structured form of the self-report, necessary to ensure some conformity between the kinds of data collected by the self-reporters and to ensure relevance to the central concerns of the research, was rather cumbersome for descriptions of some infant classes and vertically grouped classes. In such cases the self-reporters usually just abandoned the proformas and wrote freehand accounts.

But the in-service spin-offs of having some teachers in a school taking part in an exercise like this were frequently reported. There was an increased likelihood of inter-staff discussion about the subjects to be covered in topic work and how to teach the material, and of longer-term curriculum planning. In a three-teacher school where two teachers were involved, it was remarked of the effect on the non-participant teacher: 'The idea of Paula putting her coat on and going with pupils to the woods in the rain was unheard of before this; but now *everyone* is much more excited . . .'

CONCLUSION

This Introduction has surveyed the methods that were used to collect the data on which most of this book is based. In the next chapter we shall examine something of the history and evolution of topic work as a method of working in the primary school. The chapters that follow will illustrate cases, and will discuss the issues that can be extracted from those cases. But just two other related points must be made.

First, case studies can be used as *pure* research data. We could have reported in detail each case studied and either drawn conclusions from it or left the reader to interpret as he would. In this book we have not adopted this strategy, though it would be appropriate enough.

Rather, because the Schools Council project was a research and development project aimed at improving practice, we have concentrated on aspects of cases that illustrate particular practice issues. Those issues themselves have been drawn from the cases; and the research data have been extracted in order to discuss the specific questions and problems highlighted in this way. In this sense this book is an example of applied research, and is of more direct relevance to practitioners than if we had adopted the former strategy. This approach has been used successfully in previous research and development work (Wragg 1983) and is often referred to as the use of 'grounded theory'.

1

The Evolution of the Topic

INTRODUCTION

In attempting to undertake the detailed studies of topic work
described in the Introduction and illustrated throughout this book,
the caseworkers ran into an immediate problem: terminology. The
problem can be seen from two perspectives. First, in our study and
in those of other works, many teachers admitted to 'doing topics'.
But what they meant by this differed widely. Second, some schools
claimed not to have any topic-orientated curriculum; but often, in
conversation, it emerged that the teachers were working on exactly
similar lines to those claiming to 'do topics'. All that set their work
apart were the labels attached to these curriculum blocks. For this
reason it was necessary to find some definition, however amorphous
and all-embracing, within which the teachers and caseworkers could
feel that they shared a common conception of the work in progress.
Sylvia Leith (in Simon and Willcocks 1981) had experienced a
similar problem in a random sample of 33 primary schools studied.
For us, too, as we set out to explore case studies of topics, it will
be useful to clarify this rather difficult area.

TERMINOLOGY AND DEFINITION

Teachers use a variety of labels, relatively indiscriminately, to
describe what might be generically called 'topic work'. These
include: topic, project, theme, integrated work, environmental
studies, humanities, centres of interest. It seems fair to make the
assumption that there are common methods of working or of teach-
ing/learning approach which link the work described by these labels.

If those methods and approaches can be identified they might form the basis of a definition of topic work.

The researchers in the questionnaire phase of our Schools Council project collected observations of topic work in action in a variety of schools, and on the basis of these observations decided that the lessons they had witnessed could be divided into five kinds. Each of these five approximate classifications could be described in a short word-picture or cameo that captured, in essence, a specific way of working. These five cameos were as follows.

Cameo 1. This class has embarked upon an interdisciplinary study of the canal system of Kendal. The teacher takes a whole-class lead lesson which is designed to draw from the children by question and answer their knowledge of the canal itself. An hour is set aside each week for a term. During this time visits are made to the canal, and the children acquire information from local sources about the local history, industrial development and wildlife of the canal. A display of poster materials and pupils' work is mounted on the classroom walls as the weeks progress.

Cameo 2. In this primary school there is a 'mathematics week'. The aim of the topic is to make all pupils more aware of numbers in their daily lives. Each morning in assembly the head sets the whole school a problem, and teachers later use class time to help children work according to age and ability on possible solutions. Some time is given over at each assembly to reviewing the previous day's puzzle. The school hall and the corridors are filled with displays, children's work and equipment which reinforce the theme. Emphasis is firmly on fun, and on the usefulness of thinking mathematically; and the display is brightly coloured and composed with an emphasis on 'things to do'.

Cameo 3. Mrs Smith gives over almost all her timetable (excluding basic skills and fixed timetable elements) to interdisciplinary topics. This term the theme is 'France'. Some older pupils have visited the country on a school trip. They show slides and talk about their experience. Using the ideas generated by the introductory talk, Mrs Smith's class draws its own flow diagram of areas of interest and possible lines of enquiry. Pupils interested in each area of the subject get together to form working groups or pairs. Throughout the next term most of the work the class does relates to the French theme: they listen to stories set in France, look at everyday life and customs, calculate in French money, cook French meals, and so on. Each working group is responsible for a short presentation on its area of special interest. On the last day of term the class entertains a French guest.

Cameo 4. Mr Brown is using topic work to explore the idea of colour in nature. His science lessons are given over for six weeks to various aspects of the subject: camouflage, display, threat, etc. Each week pupils are given a class introduction to the particular theme for the lesson. They then work individually or in pairs to find examples from the animal kingdom using the class and school reference libraries. Each pupil writes a short piece about, for example, animals' use of colour to camouflage themselves, and then uses drawings or cut-out pictures to illustrate his or her notes. Towards the end of each lesson the class comes together. Some pupils show the others what they have found out; and there is a general discussion led by the teacher to highlight the main points of the lesson.

Cameo 5. Miss Jones's class has been watching the York Mystery Plays. The teacher decides to give over two half-days a week for half a term to class production of Orton School Mystery Play. The pupils are divided into groups, each with a specific task. One group writes the script, another will act, yet another prepares and paints the props and scenery. At the end of term the whole school watches the final performance, in which everyone in Miss Jones's class has become involved, sharing jobs such as curtain-raisers, prompter and scene shifters among those who do not actually take part in the performance.

In order to assess whether the cameos bore a reasonable relationship to reality, they were included in the questionnaire (which formed part of phases 1 and 2 of the research as described in the Introduction to this book) administered to all participating teachers. The participants were given the task of deciding whether their own lessons fitted closely any of the five cameos. In all cases teachers were indeed able to recognise their style of working in one or other of the cameos; the relative percentages of teacher and head teacher respondents (to the project's initial questionnaire) claiming affinity with each cameo was as follows:

Cameo 1 44.8%
Cameo 2   3.2%
Cameo 3 21.1%
Cameo 4 26.9%
Cameo 5   1.6% (nil responses 2.4%)

The result of this experiment suggested that an initial attempt at a definition by the caseworkers was not too far wide of the mark:

Topic work includes all those areas of the curriculum (other than *basic* reading and number skills) which are explored in a thematic way. Topics may be (predominantly) scientific, mathematical, or in the field of the humanities; or they may be multi-disciplinary.

If the exercise involving the identification of the teachers' work with specific cameos carries additional messages, then the messages are these:

1. Most topic work is in fact interdisciplinary, not simply thematic.
2. Topic work involves active learning (visits, finding out from reference material).
3. The learning is likely to be in pairs or groups rather than in individual or whole-class contexts.
4. End-products in the form of presentations or displays may be typical of this approach.
5. The implicit role for the teacher is that of wise facilitator rather than of instructor.

Previous attempts at a definition of topic work have tended to be less satisfactory than the composite insight built up by the Project's caseworkers. Plowden (1967) noted 'the topic cuts across the boundaries of subjects and is treated as its nature requires without reference to subjects as such'. For the Schools Council (1972) it was 'the special study of a theme . . . which is "researched" and documented in some form or other'. Even the prestigious DES Primary Survey (1978) contained only one explicit mention of topic work, which it labelled as the thematic approach and which it described as follows:

Many primary schools used a thematic approach to the work in social studies and a wide variety of topics were [*sic*] introduced at each age level. Often the environment of the school, or a place within easy reach of it, was the focus of this kind of work, although children also studied other countries and other times. In the course of these studies material was most often drawn from historical and geographical sources, although some schools also, on occasion, chose topics of a religious dimension. (para 5.115)

These definitions are too limited because they concentrate on the *content* of topic lessons. Rance's (1968) definition was broader, but rather cumbersome in its attempt to be all-embracing. We have also to take into account both methods of teaching and learning and the kinds of philosophies which underpin these methods. In our attempts to understand more exactly what is implied by topic work we need to turn our attention for a while to these underlying philosophies.

THE PHILOSOPHY BEHIND TOPIC WORK

A topic-work approach in primary schools, widespread in the 1980s, is nevertheless no new phenomenon. The clues as to where to look for its roots are to be found in the insights revealed by the Project's questionnaire: the child-centred nature of topic work, its interdisciplinary approach, and its implied role for the teacher. These phenomena have occurred together in two famous philosophies of education: those of Rousseau and of John Dewey.

Jean Jacques Rousseau (1712–78) established a school of philosophy known as Naturalism. He declared that 'nature wants children to be children before they are men' and he adopted a stage theory of human development of a kind with which we are comparatively familiar on account of the work of psychologists such as Jean Piaget. Rousseau thought the child should be free to learn from direct experience. This maturational view of education and resulting child-centred philosophy was highly controversial in its day. It has, however, become the cornerstone of much modern theorising about primary education.

To modern primary teachers, Rousseau's dictum of discovery learning is not specially remarkable since it is so much a part of their daily presuppositions. (Of his protégé Emile, Rousseau said that he should 'not be taught science, let him discover it'.) Nevertheless, the tradition which now manifests itself in topic work cannot abandon its roots in the education of Rousseau's Emile.

19

Rousseau's philosophical model of education was re-interpreted into a school situation by the American John Dewey (1859–1952). He believed that the natural and spontaneous activities of children can be directed to educational ends, and that this is best done through problems of the children's own devising. In effect, Dewey (1910) was advocating a scientific approach: he believed children pursuing their own studies would be motivated to speculate, observe, gather information, and test out guesses or hypotheses to solve their own problems. This approach developed into a 'project method': a contractual approach to education wherein the child worked at his or her own pace on an assignment. The teacher played a consultative role rather than a didactic one. Similarities between this and the kinds of topic work deduced from the cameos set out above are obvious, and the direct line of influence upon primary education from Rousseau via Dewey to today's classroom practice is often acknowledged quite openly in texts (from Kilpatrick 1918 to Dearden 1976 and Stewart 1986), even if the effect on teachers is more unconscious (Plowden 1967, para. 510). Kilpatrick developed these ideas to embrace a four-stage model of learning from real situations through topics. The stages were:

1. The children specify what they want to know, ask questions and devise ways of finding out.
2. They consult books and develop an action plan.
3. They execute that work.
4. They present findings to others, review and make judgements.

The ethos of this philosophy, now taken so much for granted, is, typically, summed up in a few lines from Gunning *et al.* (1981):

One of the most prolific sources of such information lies within the child's own day-to-day experience. Every day the child is involved in a vast range of experiences at first hand . . . These contacts and experiences can be used very effectively by the teacher to provide the child with a developing insight into a great range of ideas, since they provide very 'concrete' pegs on which to hang important concepts . . . (pp. 83, 84)

The fact that these lines are taken from a context in which Gunning *et al.* are arguing that children can use such experiences to develop appropriate responses to society is even more significant; for Dewey's experimental school and his project methods had similar goals. The case is even more strongly put for middle schools by Henley (1984):

> We see the middle school as providing scope to nurture the development of a child's own personality at the critical point of onset of puberty . . . We therefore expect to find a focus on the personal and social growth of pupils as individuals . . . 'Subjects' are subordinate considerations . . .

So child-centred views of education are not the only philosophical pre-conditions for espousing topic work as a suitable method of teaching and learning. Topic lessons exhibit a particular attitude towards the nature of knowledge, or epistemology. The assumption is that knowledge — at least at the primary level — cannot be compartmentalised into separate subjects. Such compartmentalisation may both fail to meet face to face the questions about their world that children perceive as important and lead to inferior teaching methods (Hirst 1974). Generally, teachers would seem to grant that some *basic* knowledge of reading, writing and numeracy needs to be taught outside the topic lesson, but hold that the topic then provides a meaningful context within which such skills are used towards wider and more significant ends. In terms of epistemology, then, exponents of topic work would seem to espouse a particular view of knowledge. How they work this view out in practice may emerge in the case studies that make up the bulk of this book. Topic work, then, has philosophical undertones, by no means always articulated by, or overtly espoused in the thinking of, the teacher — undertones which are apparently, though, indispensable to its effective execution. There are implications in all this for the minute examination of the teaching/learning methods used in topic lessons, to which we will return later in the chapter.

INTENTIONS

So far, what we have been attempting to do has been to clarify the nature of the phenomenon we have called 'topic work'. We have seen that, on individual school timetables, similar kinds of topic lessons may be given quite different labels. We have discovered that topic work is characterised by some quite distinctive approaches to content and to methods of teaching and learning. We have glanced at the philosophical underpinning of these approaches. But we have to recognise that on a day-to-day basis classroom teachers are less likely to agonise about terminology, definitions and philosophy; they are more likely to think in terms of purposes and goals: in other words, to try to clarify in their own minds what are the aims and objectives of the topic. These considerations (purposes, goals, aims, objectives) are called here, simply, *intentions*. To put the matter at its most basic, the intentions of topic work are what we expect it to do for the pupil. Quite a number of writers have attempted to summarise these intentions, and some examples are opportune at this point. Lane (1981) provides the following list:

1. To enable children to pursue a topic of interest and find the necessary information from reference books and other media.
2. To encourage children to analyse the information they find and lead them towards synthesis.
3. To encourage children to organise the information they find and present it in an attractive manner using the appropriate media.
4. To enable children to develop skills in a structured way.
5. To cultivate an interest in, and appreciation of, all form of reference — libraries, museums, buildings and places of historical interest as well as books.
6. To develop the ability to participate in small groups and to acknowledge and appreciate the opinions of others.
7. To encourage curiosity and originality, and finally,
8. To develop the children's project work from literal enquiry to an inferential or evaluative approach.

Allen and Collis (1972) emphasise the need to take children outside the classroom to give their work meaning. Bolwell (1973) puts the emphasis on what children do rather than on what they know.

By comparison, in the course of the Schools Council project, the caseworkers used the phase 1 questionnaire to elicit from teachers and head teachers their responses to questions about the intentions of topic work. Out of 61 respondents, about half said that their schools had adopted a list of intentions or aims which was known to and agreed by all staff. These respondents were asked to make a list of those intentions. Items from all the lists were then rank-ordered according to the frequency of their occurrence. The result was the following 46-item checklist.

1. To cater for varying individual abilities.

2. To promote knowledge of, and appreciation for, the environment.
3. To allow practice of basic skills and concepts.
4. To encourage pupils to follow a variety of themes (without repetition).
5. To provide a forum for interdisciplinary approaches.
6. To encourage pupil curiosity, interest, enjoyment and pleasure in learning.
7. To give breadth of knowledge, information or experience.
8. To encourage pupils to question, hypothesise, investigate and make judgements.
9. To teach observation, and the ordering and recording of observations.
10. To teach the study skills of abstracting and interpreting.
11. To promote empathy and a caring attitude.
12. To teach the use of reference materials and research skills.
13. To improve the skills of vocabulary, language and communication.
14. To promote aesthetic appreciation (of the environment).
15. To foster creative expression.
16. To develop scientific methods of enquiry.
17. To encourage individual or independent work.
18. To encourage an enquiring mind.
19. To inform, within pupils' levels of concrete experience and understanding.
20. To promote group work.
21. To serve as a vehicle for written work.
22. To increase the relevance of the curriculum.
23. To teach an appreciation of patterns and relationships.
24. To encourage the skills of the individual subject disciplines.
25. To encourage discussion.
26. To encourage the use of imagination and insight.
27. To develop logical thinking.
28. To increase pupils' opportunities for reading.
29. To use the expressive mode in music and drama.
30. To provide a wide variety of approaches to a theme.
31. To encourage pupils to produce a finished product.
32. To develop presentation skills.
33. To provide display for the whole school to share.
34. To encourage pupils to read and listen to each other's work.
35. To allow each child an element of choice in the way he participates.

36. To enable the use of a variety of media presentation.
37. To encourage the use of initiative.
38. To extend and enliven the timetable.
39. To broaden the scope for the teacher's teaching skills.
40. To examine man's past and present effects on the environment.
41. To learn and practise a variety of ways for collecting data.
42. To encourage higher-order reading skills.
43. To ensure a progression in skill development.
44. To develop practical skills.
45. To promote the use of materials in creative work.
46. To develop social skills and qualities.

Teachers, then, may not philosophise about topic work but they can articulate in some detail what they believe it will achieve in the learning experienced by their pupils. Implicit in the second checklist, at least, is the thought that topic work brings about learning through particular routes: it is a means of organising classroom life in a meaningful way. The nature of some of that organisation is explored in the next few pages.

TOPIC WORK: A WAY OF ORGANISING

Subject matter around maturational stages

We have seen that one attraction of topic work for teachers — but one not necessarily consciously espoused by them — is a philosophical one: the approach accords with an integrated view of knowledge popular in primary schools. This view has become particularly associated with the Plowden Report, and is summed up in paragraph 540:

> The idea of flexibility has found expression in a number of practices, all of them designed to make good use of the interest and curiosity of children, to minimize the notion of subject matter being rigidly compartmental, and to allow the teacher to adopt a consultative, guiding, stimulating role rather than a purely didactic one.

Plowden goes on at some length to exemplify what is summarised in this seminal passage. The influence of the examples on subsequent practice in schools across the nation is obvious. The theme of transport is quoted (para. 540) as a suitable topic for children. Starting lessons by using first-hand experiences of the physical environment of the school is advocated (para. 543). Visits outdoors to crops, ditches, woods and verges are suggested (543). Building sites, museums, local shops, traffic counts and exploring sewage works are, it is said, available as starting points for town children (544). Parks, buses, classroom pets — the list is instantly recognisable twenty years on (546–8).

The implication of all this is that the subject matter of education evolves, for primary children, from immediate starting points in first-hand experiences. Thus curriculum content is 'hung on the pegs' of these experiences. By definition, the overall content of a lesson or series of lessons becomes evolutionary: one can't determine, for example, whether it will snow tomorrow and if so whether the pupils will 'take off' from this point. The end-product, if they do 'take off', may also contain elements of mystery: the teacher cannot predict with absolute certainty whether the thinking will go in the direction of measuring volumes of melting snow or drawing snow-laden landscapes. So we move closer to a definition of what Plowden means by flexibility in this context. It is the ability of the teacher to anticipate, prepare for, encourage and pursue as many relevant avenues of thinking as emerge spontaneously from the children's excitement with the snow. In traditional terms these avenues may, or may not, provide the children with insights that might be labelled scientific, aesthetic, linguistic or mathematical. What is important — and it is surprising that Plowden does not give a passing mention to John Dewey at this point — is the *discovery* by the child of the experience of snow: 'The sense of personal discovery influences the intensity of a child's experience, the vividness of his memory and the probability of effective transfer of learning' (para. 549).

Topic work (Plowden calls it project work) is, on this view, a way of planning and organising teaching material. The criticism to which this approach is most vulnerable is its very strength, that is, that it relies on spontaneity. For example, it is hard for such potentially random triggers to learning to be moulded into a rounded curriculum. Plowden already had the seeds of the solution to the problem. The report advocated the compilation by schools of brief schemes and of lists of themes and experiences that had proved successful. These could be sifted and revised as required, while detailed syllabus planning was to be shunned as too prescriptive. But the goals of flexibility and openness to curriculum content idealised by Plowden were a hard pill to swallow since they gave no reassurance to heads or advisers who felt accountable for curriculum matters to the wider world; they did little to bolster the work of weak teachers; they failed to guide and induct new teachers or those with less than the required sensitivity and imagination. It was easier, if not in Plowden's terms as educationally desirable, to formalise the structures of curriculum. The successful themes or topics were repeated, and became the new wisdom, the *fait accompli* of primary curriculum. Interestingly, we can track the process by which this happened in one specific curriculum area; but first it may be as well to digress for a moment lest it be thought that a Plowden curriculum was wholly without a theoretical substructure to inform it.

We have seen that topic work in the 1980s, albeit unconsciously, could be seen to rest on a particular epistemology. In the same way, the Plowden curriculum rested heavily on a specific view of educational psychology — the Piagetian. Piaget's work demonstrated, despite doubts cast on it in some quarters, the existence of psychological stages of development. The stages are well known:

0–2 years	sensori-motor stage
c. 2–7 years	pre-operational stage
7/8–11/12 years	concrete operational stage
11/12–15 years	logical or formal reasoning stage

Robin Alexander (1984) has expressed reservations about this approach to conceptualising the primary child and the approach to teaching at this age. Nevertheless, he acknowledges the strength of its appeal. Undoubtedly, implicit in Plowden is the use of this theory of maturation as the yardstick against which the concrete experiences of the child could be turned into appropriate learning experiences (para. 522). In this psychological theory of stages, and in the concept of flexibility of a curriculum derived from concrete experiences in the immediate present, there is a potent mix that spells topic or project; by contrast, in the inability of some teachers to cope with open-endedness is the necessity to identify and define suitable learning experiences for children of this age and how to exploit them. These processes, because of the vagaries of the 1944 Education Act, can be seen at work most clearly in the evolution of syllabuses of religious education in the later 60s and early 70s.

Religious education is the only curriculum area which, by law, must be covered by a syllabus approved by each LEA. In the late

60s and early 70s a spate of such syllabuses was produced. Goldman (1964, 1966) had exposed contemporary abstract RE teaching to the glare of concrete Piagetian scrutiny. As a result syllabus after syllabus in RE (Humberside (1981), ILEA (1968), Kent (1968), Northampton (1980)) was revised to be full of topics — usually re-named 'life themes' under the influence of Jean Holm (1975) — considered as suitable in immediacy and stage-level for primary children. 'Hands', 'People who help us', 'Water', 'Sheep and shepherds', 'Spring' — these and other topics became the material for the, by now, predetermined 'spontaneous' experiences of the Plowden generation of primary pupils.

Topic work can, then, be or become a way of organising learning experiences and/or materials. Under the influence of Plowden the subject base of primary learning tended to be broadened. Notice that there is nothing specifically and exclusively religious about the topics from RE syllabuses quoted in the last paragraph. Primary learning was becoming more interdisciplinary, or integrated — a concept to which we will return later in the chapter. Meanwhile the growing persuasion of Piaget was emphasising concrete starting points in the primary curriculum. Both these influences were having a profound effect on the way teachers organised content into topics. But Piaget, along with other cognitive psychologists, was having another effect on teachers' thinking about the intentions of topic work.

Thinking skills

Piaget had alerted teachers to the ways in which children progress in thinking skills, and the temptation may have been to limit the diet offered to pupils as a means of keeping work within their capabilities. But others were exploring the nature of thinking or were trying in practical terms to see how far the ablest primary pupils were able to grasp difficult work. In the late 1960s and throughout the 1970s there was a renewal of interest in the able child (Ogilvy 1973); while Piaget had explored norms of thinking for specific age-ranges, others (such as De Bono 1976 and Getzels and Jackson 1963) had concentrated on the extremes of understanding and insight to which the ablest child could aspire. Some of the debate centred around 'types' of thinking: creativity versus intelligence for example. Some energy was expended on measuring thinking or on hierarchies of thought; but many workers settled for the Bloom (1956) taxonomy:

Recall
Comprehension
Application
Analysis
Synthesis
Evaluation

This provided a ready measure of the 'levels' of thinking to which children might aspire, and had the advantage that the teacher could use the categories in planning lessons. A brief example will suffice.

Joanne wants to study bird life. In conversation with the teacher she talks through some things she has discovered from the Observer's book she has at home (*recall*). She explains that the bluetits which come to the feeder may not be the same pair each time: some bird-watchers have ringed their garden birds and found that up to about 200 may visit a single garden (*comprehension*). The teacher asks her to try to find out whether the same is true of the blackbirds that come for the food which the class scatters on the patio outside the classroom window. She gathers together some classmates, each one detailed to watch a particular bird, and between them they discover several pairs coming from different directions to feed (*application*). As the spring wears on, one pair of bluetits nests in the box hanging under the roof overhang of the classroom. The nest is packed with young birds and the teacher asks Joanne to speculate as to why there are so many (*analysis*). Joanne thinks it is because the local cats get so many, and other pupils contribute other theories. In the hedge in the school garden the blackbirds are nesting, too. They have fewer young. The teacher encourages Joanne to discover why things are different for blackbirds. She concludes that blackbirds are better protected owing to the female's camouflaged plumage, which leads to more effective survival for the chicks (*synthesis*), because the nest is less easily spotted. Finally, Joanne sets out to compare survival rates at local blackbird nests by finding out which kinds of locations (natural, man-made) are most often attacked by predators (*evaluation*).

This example illustrates how a teacher can keep track of pupils' thinking using Bloom's six categories of cognition. Of course, cognition is not the only kind of valid learning (affective and psycho-motor skills are important, too); but it is obviously central to much school work. The Bloomian system, or some adaptation of it, is obviously a helpful tool and gives a useful set of constructs against which to track progress in topic work where, unlike in mathematics or reading, there are few, if any, commercial schemes available. The use of this system applied to topic work is exemplified in the work of Lane (1981), specifically in his Appendix 4, 'A staged skill development programme for project work in the primary school'. In the previous section it was argued that subject matter was gradually organised into themes or topics under the influence of the Piagetian insight that teachers should begin from where the child was in his or her understanding and experience. This trend led, it was suggested, to life themes in RE teaching, for example. But the increasing emphasis on analytical approaches to thinking skills perhaps encouraged another trend, towards a more formalised curriculum in topic work — a curriculum in which 'an expert' beyond the classroom had taken some of the uncertainty away by building the thinking skills into a particular curriculum material or framework. Thus we see the evolution of the topic progress in the direction of the relatively prescriptive number or reading scheme. Examples of this type might be the Schools Council *Integrated Studies Project* (1973) or Blyth's *Place and time with children aged 5–9* (1984).

Methods of teaching

Let us then summarise what has been said so far in this chapter about the evolution of topic teaching. Topic work is a phenomenon teachers recognise by its interdisciplinary nature, its active and experiential learning based on Piagetian principles, and its emphasis on discovery learning by pupils. As we have suggested, these characteristics imply a particular approach to teaching. This section examines some aspects of teaching method as they impinge on topic teaching.

Barker-Lunn (1984) noted that 'nearly half the teachers [in a sample of 732 schools] made provision for individual or topic work at least once a week. This involves children in carrying out a piece of research and producing a report and often encompasses work in several curricular areas.' Reporting back, individual projects and display of results represent common learning activities and imply peer-group teaching and the role of the teacher as facilitator. Implicit, too, are individualised learning and group work. Deanne Boydell (1979) investigated the nature and function of these classroom groups.

Boydell points out that Plowden had recommended the formation of small groups at roughly the same stage, but on a transitory basis and not as a device for hidden streaming. She noted in her own studies that teachers tended to have 'regular' groups of pupils who habitually sat together, but that transactions between teachers and pupils in these groups tended to be on an individual rather than a group basis. This insight encouraged her to look more closely at teacher–group transactions, and also at what other pupils in the class were doing when their group was not the focus of the teacher's attention. She came to the following conclusions:

1. Unsupervised groups of pupils do tend to stay on task most of the time, and this, coupled with informal methods of teaching, is productive of learning.
2. Most verbal contacts between pupils involved only two individuals, usually of the same sex.
3. Most verbal contacts between pupils are short-lived: less than 25 seconds in duration. This might militate against a significant level of peer-group learning.

Boydell's findings are ambiguous. They suggest that group work is *potentially* a useful learning tool but that it may not be effectively utilised on the grounds that teachers are not necessarily sufficiently aware of the dynamics of the groups they cause to be formed. The cases described later in this book examine in some more detail the relationships between whole-class, group and individualised learning. What seems relatively certain, however, is that the prevalence of group work lent itself to at least some kinds of group-based topic work in which the teacher could keep initiatives by dividing up activities so that not all children in the class were simultaneously occupied on the same task. This form of organisation is often easily justified, too, on affective rather than educational grounds. Boydell's work is specially interesting in this context since it casts some doubt upon the validity of this affective justification.

The other major issue relating to teaching method is a vexed one: the definition of teaching style and the relationship of teaching style to topic work. Here the most controversial issues concern Bennett's (1976) work on teaching styles and pupil progress. At its simplest the theme of this research was that formal teaching produced more effective learning than informal teaching: a conclusion which caused consternation in many post-Plowden primary schools and one which gave great exaltation to the would-be authors of Primary Black Papers. However, the issue was not clear cut. Bennett's classifications of style were rapidly questioned. More significantly, his statistics were re-worked and called into question. The debate produced over a hundred articles in education journals in the following few years and is too vast to summarise here. Suffice it to say that no definitive evidence on the effectiveness emerged (Aitken, Bennett and Hesketh 1981), though a subsequent study of the most effective 'informal' teacher in Bennett's sample, by Wragg (1978), showed that the most likely component of the effectiveness was the ability to make rapid and appropriate inter-personal contacts with the pupils to guide their work. From the point of view of topic work, if 'formal' teaching is equated with long periods of class-taught literacy and numeracy, then topic work would be the prerogative of 'informal' teachers; but in practice the evidence of many studies is that teachers change style to suit the activity in progress, and even Bennett had to label one style 'mixed'.

After Bennett, the ORACLE research at Leicester University developed a stylistic analysis to describe 'types' of teaching. Their categories were:

individual monitors
class enquirers
group instructors
changers: habitual
changers: rotating

Their work is interesting because it began to explore the relationships between teaching style and the learning style of pupils (Galton, Simon and Croll 1980a, 1980b).

What Bennett's work, the resulting controversies and the ORACLE research all have in common is that they demonstrate that teaching style is *one* significant component of classroom life, which works in ways as yet not wholly understood. For the present, the point of view that is not possible is the simple equation: topic-work methods = informal teaching style. What can be said with a degree of certainty is that topic work presupposes certain kinds of enquiry-based pupil learning and therefore a certain range of teacher behaviours in response. The subtleties have not yet been probed adequately, and in an oblique way perhaps some of the cases in this book will show the range of styles teachers bring to topic lessons. Perhaps it would be fairer to conclude that topic work fits less into a style and more into an ethos.

CONTEXTUAL INFLUENCES AND TOPIC TEACHING

During the course of this chapter the argument has been pursued that topic teaching is a distinctive approach to teaching in the primary classroom and that this method of working occupies a significant proportion of time for primary children. This situation was certainly the case in the East Midlands schools surveyed in the current research, where from 10 per cent to 75 per cent of pupils' time was spent on topics in individual schools. These findings were echoed by the ORACLE team at Leicester University (Galton *et al.* 1980a), who suggested that 15 per cent of teaching time might typically be spent on topic work. If these figures are reasonably accurate then it also has to be hypothesised that topic work is related to a wider context of teaching, and that in any study of the evolution of topic work the contextual influences need examination. We would argue here that there are three important sets of contextual influences on topic work, and we shall examine each of these in turn.

The traditional role of the primary teacher

Traditionally, primary teachers have been generalists. Whether this has been substantially because the schools demanded such teachers or because the nature of the applicants propelled them to favour this kind of approach is hard to say: both factors were probably at work. Research into teacher eduction shows, for example, that, in the recent past, recruits into primary education were more likely to come from working-class families than were those into the prestigious areas of secondary education (Robbins 1963; Isaac 1969); and this was particularly true of the men (Ashley, Cohen and Slatter 1967). Motives for wanting to teach often included 'love of children' (Wragg 1967), and perhaps unsurprisingly, therefore, teaching as a profession was a first choice of half the girls in a large sample surveyed by de Lacey and Pryor (1976), but of only 12.5 per cent of boys. Teaching is often a 'second best' career (Hellawell and Smithers 1973) but one which fits well for women having young children of their own. In previous decades women have been less persuaded towards academic courses and subject specialisms, and before the universality of BEd courses may well have opted for shorter and less specialist Certificate in Education courses as a path into the profession. Society in general, and head teachers specifically, have probably (at least until the late 70s and early 80s) favoured the appointment of women teachers for young children. If this scenario is correct, then it would seem that in the last few decades the demands of schools and the preferences and inclinations of the potential teaching force have tended to merge into a generalist view of the primary teacher, who will typically have been an upwardly mobile higher working-class or middle-class girl, opting for less demanding and less specialist academic training than her male counterpart in a situation where, until recently, it has been relatively easy to return to work to a convenient job when the family has reached the age of about four to five years. This view is an historical, not a sexist, one — and times have changed. But schools are slow to adapt and evolve. Much of the thinking about primary education, and a good deal of its practice at the classroom level, has been by teachers whose backgrounds are as described. It cannot be doubted that such teachers, with their strong generalist inclinations, would have been attracted by the child-centred thinking already outlined in this chapter and by the approaches to teaching that allowed their generalist talent most rein. Topic teaching undoubtedly lent itself to those inclinations.

Mixed-ability and mixed-age grouping

Primary classes embracing children of ages and abilities across the whole spectrum have been normal since the 1870 Education Act. In village schools with small populations and one teacher, there was no alternative; indeed, it was in such contexts that the generalist teachers referred to above had their origins. Schools of this kind may be rarer now, the school bus may have turned tots into commuters, but such schools do still exist. Primary schools have always substantially reflected the communities they serve. But there were exceptions. The advent of the secondary school for those beyond elementary school age, and the classification of schools to include grammar schools at post-11+ selection put pressures on rural and urban, small and large primaries alike to adopt age and ability stratification as means of organising classes. With the demise of the grammar school in favour of the comprehensive from the 1960s onwards primary schools have been freer or perhaps more compelled to revert to mixed-age and/or mixed-ability groupings for pupils. Some economic and social trends have made this reversion more attractive or at least more pressing: for example, falling rolls and a relative decline in cash for teachers and resources. The whole question was given impetus by Jim Callaghan's 'Great Debate' speech in 1976.

The most recent survey of mixed-age classes in primary schools was carried out for the Schools Council by Bennett, O'Hare and Lee (1982). The researchers rightly make the point that any form of classroom organisation must be matched by an adequate philosophy and appropriate teaching methods in order to be successful. Bennett's survey made some important discoveries about mixed-age classes in the 1,500 primary schools questioned:

1. Small rural schools adopt mixed-age organisation out of necessity.
2. Quoted reasons for adopting this form of organisation included more effective use of resources, space and staff, and to increase pupils' feelings of security and stability.
3. Mixed-age organisation is increasing, mainly because of falling rolls, but the precise form of mixing ages is dynamic and evolving.
4. Pupils' abilities are used as a means of assigning them to classes of mixed age.
5. Of head teachers questioned, 49 per cent saw 'some' or 'great' difficulties in teaching maths in a mixed-age class, 44 per cent in teaching English, 49 per cent in teaching science, 42 per cent in teaching history, 41 per cent in story-telling and 41 per cent in teaching geography. By contrast, only 33 per cent anticipated problems with topic and project work.

These findings suggest that teachers use topic work as a means of organising learning which, quite apart from any educational merit, helps with the management of the classroom. The same kind of hint is to be found in Bennett *et al.* (1980): 'Teachers usually set aside mornings to work on the basics and afternoons for project and creative activities, a practice very common in open plan schools.'

We have noted in passing in this section that ability is one criterion used by teachers to assign pupils to mixed-age classes, but that streamed classes of similar-aged pupils had been the norm in the days of grammar schools. A substantial number of pupils of primary age find themselves, however, in classes of similar-aged pupils but of mixed ability. In the 1970s mixed-ability teaching attracted wide interest in the emerging comprehensives (Wragg 1976; Sands and Kerry 1981; Reid 1981) but was so commonplace in primary schools as to be considered the norm. Blyth (in Cohen *et al.* 1982) attempts to account for this by suggesting it was 'generally considered that non-streaming was quite compatible with the withdrawal of pupils either for remedial work or for minority interests'.

What is certain, however, is the following: whether primary pupils are assigned to classes by age or by ability, once there, teachers have to adopt strategies for administering their work. Central to these strategies is the subdivision of the class into more or less permanent working groups. What is both well documented and universally acknowledged by teachers is that these working groups themselves may include pupils who are assigned on the basis of ability: which indicates hidden streaming. In most schools the labels ('top', 'bottom') have gone; but the stratification remains. Other common methods of assignment to groups may include friendship choice or the teacher's deliberate attempt at gender, social or ability mix. In all cases, though, the group as a basis for work is central to primary classes. The group is one important focus for topic or project work, and the tendency of primary teachers to group pupils for organisational purposes may itself be a spur to the use of the topic as a teaching medium.

The cynical view on all this has been summed up in a classic statement by John Eggleston (1980):

> Teachers faced with mixed ability classes, integrated curricula, wide differences in motivation in a single classroom, turn thankfully to the project as the one method of organization wherein subject boundaries and differences in levels can be blurred, where it is still legitimate to assign different tasks to children of different abilities and where all can be deemed to finish work at the same time ready to move on to the next project.

Architecture, time and resources

There can be little doubt that a further reason why topic work flourished in the post-Plowden era was the move by school architects towards open-plan schools. Teachers are quite overt about the need to adapt the work which they do to the situations, including the physical situations, in which they find themselves. The open-plan classroom had several predictable effects on teachers and children: it increased movement, it heightened noise levels, and it meant that some re-organisation of staffing for classes would inevitably result. It was probably easier to use another teacher as a resource in an open-plan school — and almost without exception LEAs put extra money into audio-visual and library back-up for their new creations. Topic work was thus a more logical way of working than the more traditional compartmented approaches. There was a new freedom for children to move around to retrieve information, and less emphasis on sitting still. Flexi-space could also mean flexi-timetabling. More tasks were set children individually: it just wasn't possible to conduct whole-class expositions and exercises.

This summary does not necessarily imply that teachers (or even children) liked or adapted to the change. Many did not. Ways of creating private living spaces within large areas were invented with rapidity. But for a while at least the combination of events surrounding this trend in architecture had to be coped with, and for some at least topic work appeared to be the answer.

THE TOPIC AND THE PRIMARY CURRICULUM

The method adopted by this chapter so far has been to survey influences within primary education that have contributed to the development of the topic as a means of working in classrooms and to suggest how topic work has evolved in response to these influences. This section, then, tries to analyse the interrelationships between topic work and the rest of the primary curriculum.

There can be little doubt that the primary curriculum is orientated towards basic skills, and that this emphasis is a direct result of parental and social pressure. Among the basic skills, reading is seen as most crucial because it is the key to so much other learning. Some literature on topic work, therefore, is dominated by reading skills. The topic is seen as fundamentally an opportunity for children to glean information from reference books; thus 'advanced reading skills' are paramount. Typical of this genre is Lane (1981). This booklet reports a Schools Council project on topic work; of the 31 pages of the report itself, 18 mention reading and many of them are wholly or substantially on the themes of reading skills or reading resources. Of Lane's 62 references, 30 (48 per cent) are related to reading or reading skills. There is much here that is valuable.

Lane, for example, spends much energy on defining the skills pupils need to cope effectively with book-based information-gathering. He notes that each topic will extend the pupil through its specific vocabulary; that pupils must be able to cope with library classification systems; that they must acquire selection skills in choosing important and relevant information, in scanning and skimming, in adjusting reading rate and in seeking main ideas in a text. He emphasises specific abilities: note-taking, study techniques, looking up new words, making plans before committing work to paper. He identifies the more sophisticated needs of children in evaluating, interpreting and making editorial judgements relating to what they have read. He also puts information-gathering into a context of communication: the pupil must learn to pay attention to lay-out, style, vocabulary, proof-reading and even the medium of communication adopted.

From a teacher's point of view Lane also has a good checklist by which to judge the quality and suitability of classroom texts. This checklist includes:

- print style and clarity
- good illustrations
- effective headings
- lack of dense blocks of print
- handleability of the book itself
- the absence of jargon

Scepticism about this approach is not about the soundness of the advice — it is very sound. Rather, it relates to a feeling that the underlying assumption is that topic work may simply be fact-grubbing from reference books, a sterile corruption of the Plowden ideal of hands-on learning emerging from the real interest and excitement of the child. The same kind of attitude underpinned one of the few oblique references to topic work in the Primary Survey (DES 1978): 'The curriculum as a whole provides many opportunities for pupils to *apply* basic skills, and it contains *other elements* that are important in their own right' (para. 8.24: our italics). To these 'other elements' we shall return in a little while; but for the moment it is important to note that the authors' own Schools Council project also encountered a widespread attitude among teachers that topic work was a practice ground, *not a jumping-off point*, for significant learning in the basic skills. It is a view we shall question later, in reporting the case studies.

For some, then, topic work is inextricably (if in our view inadequately) linked to basic skills, in particular to reading and partially to language development. This was the view even of HMI in DES 1978, who saw the topic as also embracing other important elements. What are these? HMI lists them as 'work on plants, animals, and man-made objects and materials'. This we interpret as a loose definition of environmental education. Environmental education was firmly grounded in the rationale of the Plowden Report. In the post-Plowden era publishers were quick to exploit this area as one in which to produce resources. Thus Miles (1983) notes that from 1969 Blandford produced eighteen titles for the Nuffield Foundation Resources for Learning project, 'Approaches to Environmental Studies'. Over eighty themes were illustrated in Jeremiah (1972), and Mills and Boon published a series called 'On Location' (1973). Even Bullock (1975) stressed the importance of the environment as a stimulus to reading. The trend has continued and escalated since. To give it impetus society, too, has become more environmentally conscious. One has only to note the increasing efforts of peace campaigners, the rise of the so-called Green Parties in international politics, the impact of the Chernobyl disaster and so on, to realise that teachers may well be using the broad issues of environment and conservation as starting points for learning. Indeed for quite some time attempts have been made to base a major curriculum element on this area of knowledge. The most detailed, structured and successful of these is probably Cast (1979). In this context, what is significant about this attempt is that the whole approach is topic-based. Indeed, environmental education lends itself to this method of organising information and of learning so that, in our questionnaire study of the 'Developing pupils' thinking through topic work' project, we found that many teachers regarded topic work and environmental studies as synonymous or at least as more or less inextricable from each other.

But in the post-Plowden era environmental education is not the only area of knowledge to have seen the potential of topic-work approaches to its particular subject matter. All the traditional 'disciplines' other than literacy and numeracy have tended to move in this direction — though by no means exclusively. In history Joan Blyth (1984) has adopted source-based and thematic approaches. The best kind of history for the primary child is very much based on phenomena available in the immediate environment, on real objects that can be touched and seen: canals, mills, churches, castles. The work links up to the cognitive skills mentioned earlier, involving the sifting of evidence, the deduction of information from sources, the editing out of the irrelevant and the making of judgements on the evidential base.

The sort of history described here is perhaps biased towards the local, that is, the environmental. In a very real sense the environmentally based topic has taken over from subject-specific history: and the same is true of other subject areas. Cast's environmental studies programme is substantially science-based; and this, too, is part of the trend. In the aesthetic areas — art, craft, drama, music — the move is to use these aesthetic domains to illustrate, reinforce and sensitise children around the broader theme of the current topic under consideration. This was one of the clear findings of the questionnaire of our Schools Council project, and it was illustrated in some of the case studies.

In curriculum terms, then, the topic has tended to subsume all but basic literacy and numeracy. The traditional disciplines do contribute both to subject matter and methodology, but the topic is what gives coherence to what is studied. Whether this trend has been adequately thought through, whether the traditional disciplines have lost out and whether the movement is soundly based on a rational philosophy are questionable, and we shall explore these matters again in later chapters.

THE TOPIC AS A TASK AND AS AN END-PRODUCT

Plowden is probably as responsible as any other authority for the widespread practice of turning work, especially topic work, into attractive classroom displays. Certainly the Report emphasised the importance of an attractive learning environment: so teachers provided stimulus materials to make the current classroom work attractive. The contributions of pupils came later, when the topic had begun to mature. These pupil productions are usually the tasks carried out by children and the results of their labours; only occasionally are they merely cosmetic. If these completed tasks have a value of their own, then, they are as the tangible — and presumably assessable — end-products of classroom endeavour. Such endeavour may be by a group or by an individual. Gunning *et al.* (1981) rightly see these tasks as often the results of enquiries carried out. Such tasks can be classified using Bloom's (1956) taxonomy, and some mention has been made of this earlier in the chapter. It is, therefore, possible to make cognitive measures of what pupils have achieved in topic work. Though the practice is not widespread, it is documented in the literature of primary practice. Clough *et al.* (1985) note that to many teachers 'topic work and assessment seem odd bedfellows', since they see the values in social and emotional terms more than in cognitive ones.

39

Clough *et al.* designed and taught two topics ('Industrial Revolution' and 'Brazil') to top juniors. They attempted through discussion and experience to extract possible methods of evaluation of pupils' work in topic lessons. They drew several conclusions:

- that conventional assessment of terminal written work with a single grade or comment is inappropriate;
- that 'soft' (i.e. formative) data are useful;
- that assessment methods have to be specifically appropriate to curricular content;
- that assessments should be made of other activities than writing (e.g. oral work, drama);
- that pupils can be usefully involved in assessment;
- that assessments should be recorded.

Though this work is extremely small-scale the problems which Clough *et al.* encountered are almost more interesting than their conclusions, and are certainly ripe for debate; indeed, later parts of this book may contribute to that debate. These problems included the statement that: 'We found it . . . impossible, for example, to formulate other than the vaguest curricular objectives *which applied across different topics*' (our italics). The planning process, too, lent itself to some debate:

> *It seemed artificial to sit down and list objectives before making detailed lesson plans*; also any list which represents a valid picture of a teacher's aspirations for the outcomes of a topic would include a wide variety of broad and narrower (some content-specific) objectives. Our lists were too long to be practically useful.

Finally, the italicised passage in the next quotation must also give cause for concern, though most teachers would accept the correctness of the remainder:

> *We found it impracticable to devise methods of assessment for all the objectives. We had to select, and this we did on the basis of the priorities and inclinations of individual teachers within the context of the particular topic chosen. Previously, the assessment of topic work had concentrated on the quality of presentation of pupils' work. Bearing in mind the purposes of assessment, it became obvious that this was inadequate.* Many of the ideas we

subsequently discussed could not yield 'hard' assessment data on pupils but might either influence teaching approaches or serve themselves as learning devices. This 'spilling over' of assessment into teaching was, we decided in the end, both inevitable and proper. We addressed some radical questions about assessment methods in the contexts of the chosen topics. These included: What should be assessed? How can we best assess that particular intended outcome? When should we assess the work of the topic? Who should do the assessing?

So far, this chapter has attempted to review some of the literature of topic work and to trace the influence of changing primary practice in the evolution of the topic as a way of working. Clough *et al.* probably reflect the confusion that many teachers feel about assessing pupils' topic work and as such their work may be a reasonable statement about the state of the art. The failure of teachers to keep records of any kind was picked up by the questionnaire research carried out for our Schools Council project: 42 per cent of our sample admitted to not keeping any record whatsoever, and less than 10 per cent recorded *children's achievements* (as opposed to work covered, for example). In the evolutionary process, assessment in topic work has a long way to go to catch up.

CONCLUSION

This chapter was headed 'The evolution of the topic'. As in human evolution, there are some quite precise clues but some gaps in the evidence or ambiguities. Some kind of summary can be made with reasonable certainty, however.

Topic work in today's primary schools has its roots ultimately in the Naturalist and Deweyan schools of thought. These have been interpreted by Plowden and given psychological underpinning by Piaget. Topic work is, characteristically, interdisciplinary; it is about hands-on experience in the environment. The teacher is less didactic than facilitating and children often tend to work in active investigative groups even if not on group tasks. Topics may be open-ended, flowing in directions determined by children's interests rather than by predetermined schemes of work.

In these senses the teaching style could be labelled 'informal', but more precise investigation is required of the parameters of informal style. Subject areas have been re-interpreted into thematic approaches, again often environmentally based, probably by teachers who feel more at home as generalists than as specialists. Some at least of the themes of these environmental studies may reflect changing values in society. In the evolutionary process little systematic thought has been given to assessment and evaluation of topic work, or of children's achievement in topic lessons. Topic work is popular with teachers for good reasons (for example, children find it interesting and motivating) though some topic work may be the result of organisational convenience, such as a response to falling rolls or lack of adequate facilities and resources. The topic is seen as a vehicle for the practice of basic skills.

In the rest of this book we shall be looking at topic work in action through extracts from case studies generated by the Schools Council project 'Developing pupils' thinking through topic work'. In the process we shall be trying to raise issues about how effectively teachers use this methods of curriculum organisation and this teaching/learning method. Evolution is a dynamic process: what we are trying to do through this study, and any resulting debate, is to encourage fellow professionals to take that evolution a stage or two further by investigating through extracts from cases some real classroom problems and issues. The result should be, for the reader, some hardening up and re-definition of professional practice.

2

An Interesting Case

THE INTENTION

In the Introduction we suggested that case studies of topic work in action could serve two purposes. First, to provide *pure* research data, i.e. information about *what* is happening, so that it can be subjected to scrutiny with a view to a deeper understanding of the ways in which classrooms *do* function. Secondly, to begin to provoke exploration and discussion about *why* these things are happening — motives, intentions, present effectiveness and possible alternatives — i.e. the *developmental* aspect of research.

This chapter describes in some detail a 'case' of topic work in action. the case illuminates both the pure and the developmental approaches to research. It will immediately strike a chord with teachers, since it will describe a classroom and classroom events which are familiar to them in their daily professional lives. As the case develops, however, it will do more than this: *it will raise, directly or by implication, a whole series of key questions or issues about approaches to topic-work teaching and learning.* These issues will, in turn, be explored in the rest of this book, using examples from further case studies to expand and exemplify the argument.

For the moment, however, we can concentrate our attention on an interesting case of topic work at Roseborough primary school where Mrs Byrd, the year-group leader of year two, teaches a class of eight-year-olds.

ROSEBOROUGH SCHOOL AND ITS ORGANISATION

Mrs Byrd's topic work cannot be studied effectively without

reference to the context in which she and the pupils work; hence any sound case study must begin with a description of the school and its organisation.

Roseborough primary school (7–11, NOR 500) has its frontage along a crescent of post-war terraced housing in Midlands redbrick. Its original core is typical of school buildings of the early 1900s; but it was a period of expanding population for this bustling market town, itself the meeting-place of busy crossroads. Little by little the school expanded, the east and west wings following the crescent to leave an elongated chain of classrooms linked by a covered external walk-way on the side away from the road. Even this was not adequate for the prosperous 50s and 60s; so a flat-roofed block of classrooms, kitchen and staffroom were added on the opposite side of the playground. The windswept expanse of the playing fields and the elongated geography of the buildings make movement on the site inconvenient in winter.

Though the catchment population for Roseborough is, as the head puts it, 'mixed in the nicest sense', the unsupportive nature of many homes and the lower-than-average ability of many pupils is reflected in the school's EPA status. This means that there were, during the study period, two ancillary workers in the school in addition to the teaching staff.

Mr Berry, the headmaster, exudes a calm professionalism. His smartness, deep human concern and clear thinking seem reflected in the school about him, in the staff–pupil relationships and in the classroom resource collections and displays. The case-study methodology we adopted involved a tape-recorded interview with the head teacher about his topic-work provision, and so it is possible to allow him to speak for himself about the way that learning through topic work is managed at Roseborough.

Thirteen years ago, when I came to the school, topic work was freely chosen by individual staff. It was noticeable that if one teacher produced a good resource collection it was borrowed by everyone else — which indicated to me that planning was deficient. There seemed to be important educational skills missing in what was taught. At this time, the Welsh Environmental Project was coming to its end and I was asked to be an assessor for it. This influenced my thinking. In our system we had a free-for-all curriculum, 'wet play-time all day'. Now, the Welsh scheme was structured with definite aims and definite skills development. I was interested in a kind of middle road, because the environmental work is best geared to the needs and situation of the individual school. About this time, I appointed a new deputy to be in charge of environmental education; and so we began to write things down and to look more systematically at what our children were learning.

What emerged was a book. It's not a syllabus, but it is a means to devising a curriculum, and it does contain a rationale. *All the years round* asks key questions about man in his environment: who, why, when, where and how? It summarises teaching as: observation, analysis, deduction and possible conclusions. The approach is analytical and it works even with young children. Young children are curious — so it's a natural approach. It works differently for different teachers. Some classes are divided into working groups and the children themselves take leadership roles. Other teachers are less committed to this way of working; but in these environmental studies sessions there is always a lot of pupil–pupil and pupil–teacher dialogue, and there are always plenty of outside visitors.

Much of the information we want children to handle and use is in adult format, perhaps closeted in libraries. In this case the teachers act as intermediaries, putting it into suitable format. But wherever possible, say in a village study, we would get children to handle the census documents in their original format. And the whole curriculum is covered, too. For example, from the town census returns we did a whole week's mathematics. Drama, art, everything is covered; but we tend not to think of disciplines but of the 'primary child', and the social side is not neglected either. Balanced curriculum, like so much else, depends upon judgements made by a sensitive teacher. They don't spend the whole week on this work, the amount of time is discretionary and they will have separate sessions for basic subjects as well; but the work gives room for individuals to find an *internal* balance through environmental studies. What it does do is to change one's view of teaching. Teachers learn; they take stock, they change direction; and they learn to live a bit without the old securities.

Of course, all this has management implications. There is constant informal dialogue between staff. Our year-group structure ensures that, through frequent meetings, curriculum is monitored. We have a whole-staff training night each week, during which we look at specific skills or aspects of our teaching. Recently we reviewed our art and craft. Two talented artists ran six sessions of mainly practical work for the rest of us. After these sessions we try out new ideas, and come back to discuss them. Then, as head, I sample to check that things are going on quite well. I spend most *mornings in classrooms and I can get a pretty clear idea of what's going on. I feel my role, though, is to lead, not cajole.*

We've tried various ways to monitor progress by tracking pupils' learning. But you can measure only those things that are measurable. Many things in topic work are not measurable. We tried tracking skill-development using a tick-list; but that's arid, it doesn't tell you much about understanding. We're not convinced it measured application. Teachers currently record what they've done, pupils' reactions, their plans and a profile of the child. This may be too informal, just as the tick-list was too formal. Any system used needs to be flexible, to take account of teachers' opportunism, so there's a dilemma and we've not solved this problem. But that doesn't mean that we're not clear about some criteria. Attitudes are important, for example. Can the child stay at a task for a period of time? Has he mastered some environmental language? Can he mix, work with others? These questions, and others, have to be explored individually; it's a mistake to look at a class globally. Nor should one forget the other participants in the child's learning. The teacher needs to carry the parents along, to be sure they understand what the youngsters are getting from field trips, for example. And then there's job satisfaction for the teacher, too.

These comments represent a deep insight into the atmosphere and administration of Roseborough. In a case study the factual accuracy can be cross-checked by an observer. In this study, conversations like this one were recorded, transcribed and read by the participants, each of whom was then free to amend, add or delete things which failed to express their true intentions. In this monologue, and in all the reports which are quoted, it can be assumed, therefore, that what is reported represents a very close approximation indeed to what the case-studied teachers and the case-study workers perceived as the reality of any given situation.

This, then, is the backdrop to the case study of Mrs Byrd at work, and it is to her classroom that we now proceed.

Mrs Byrd, year-group leader and class teacher

Our case studies used questionnaires and interviews so that teachers could talk about themselves and their work in their own words:

All the years round, our environmental scheme, is a planned four-

year approach to integrated studies based on the environment. It sets out themes for all four years, 7–11. These themes are interrelated and linked throughout the child's school life; and as such it is *not* a list of set but disjointed topics for year groups of the kind one finds in some schools. Its content is wide, and we are free to omit or amend if we believe it necessary. These emendations are settled at year-group level and agreed with the head.

In the second year (my own), we take our current themes, farming and settlement, and we read and discuss the content of the work together. Obviously, there is a wealth of material within these themes which can serve to illustrate them. We may share activities such as field trips; but at other times each teacher may pursue an individual course. But *All the years round* is a philosophy of education — it asks children to deduce, analyse and conclude — so all the work will have these end-products in mind.

Having taken the themes of farming and settlement as the basis of our work at present we bear them in mind continually in our field visits, in classroom skills, in information provided, even in study skills. We teach such things as mapping, geographical formation and its effect on farming, farming methods today and how these change over time. We grow food, raise chickens and so on.

We've looked at the settlement of our town, and at present we're pursuing the same idea in a study of one of the satellite villages. So we're exploring why Roseborough was settled (this relates back to an underlying theme of this scheme, i.e. the needs of man), its relationship to our market town geographically and historically, and farming in and around Roseborough; and we're carrying out a village survey using methods that could be used in other village studies.

Throughout the work the children will come across the Celts, the Romans, the Vikings, the Danes and the Normans. This will prove to be a direct link for them to the third-year theme of 'Man the Invader' . . . They must 'do', not just listen. Emphasis changes, from art to drama or from history to wildlife, as the theme develops. But everything links to the theme itself. Even in the lessons you are observing, the work on wind and water mills is part of understanding the farming and settlement ideas, although its links with man's use of energy are picked up again in years 1 and 3.

In preparing the work that goes on in the classroom from day to day conceptual development and understanding are most important, above factual information. I believe that working in groups develops social skills and I try to ensure that pupils listen constructively to *each other. So I see myself as problem deviser, planner, leader, provider of information and advice, helper, friend and substitute parent for these eight-year-olds.*

A lesson in progress

What emerges from Mrs Byrd's account of her work is an impression of clarity about her intentions and teaching approaches. In our case studies the next task was to explore the classroom processes to see how they fulfilled these intentions. The case-study worker observed over a period of weeks and wrote appropriate case-notes of the lessons in progress. What follows is his account of one of Mrs Byrd's lessons.

A LESSON ACCOUNT

This is an account of a lesson which occupied the period from morning break to afternoon break. It covers some work in progress on the theme 'Caunton Village Survey', and involves a class of eight-year-olds in a school which has EPA status. The school buildings range across more than sixty years of architectural whim; but this classroom is a modern box, adequate but not spacious. There is a small reading corner, open-plan within the classroom. Pupils' work of recent date is hung attractively about the walls. Two long horizontal surfaces are filled with resource books and stimulus cards both around the theme itself, and of a more general nature. Plants grow, a wormery is being constructed, collections of fossils and rocks are handled by the pupils.

There is a slight air of clutter about the room: the result of too many pupils in too small a space. But there is freedom. Pupils move around to carry out their tasks; they do it in a purposeful and orderly fashion. The teacher is mobile; she doesn't need to restore order nor raise her voice in order to communicate. This is a classroom characterised by good relationships, between teacher and pupils, and between the pupils themselves. Dialogues are conversations: purposeful but informal.

> *11.00 The children enter the classroom; the teacher is present already. They are set to work from maths cards for five minutes while the teacher organises each group of pupils on the task for the session.*

This group work is distinctive. These youngsters have been trained to tackle tasks co-operatively, the leadership role within the group devolving on the pupils who seem capable of sharing this role according to the nature of the activity. The groups, once they have been given their instructions, seem able to organise themselves. Since the teacher expects and checks on task performance there cannot be any slacking. Conversations between pupils are surprisingly task-orientated.

The group tasks are assigned as follows:

Group 1
A work-card gives these instructions:

Make a windmill exactly the same as the one in the picture (i.e. draw it to scale). You must work out a way to make D = 10 cms, B measure 6 cms, and A and C measure 8 cms. *How will you do this?*

The sails must fit exactly in the centre at the top of the tower. They must be exactly 10 cms long. The door must be exactly in the middle of the bottom of the tower. *How will you work that out?* The door must measure 1½ × 3 cms. The windows are 1 cm².

Find the area of the mill's tower.

Figure 2.1

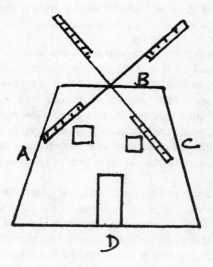

Group 2
This group is given practice in object analysis. Using a classification system already taught and available on resource cards in the room, the pupils in this group have each to analyse a series of objects such as fragments of flint, bone, clay pipe, seeds and straw discovered during the village survey.

Group 3
The group has been looking at the cog wheels in the wind and water mills during the Caunton village survey. The task is to explore how these cogs work. Pupils are provided with ply-board bases, some old jar lids, hammers and nails. They use the nails as pivots or axles to arrange wheels (lids) of various sizes on the boards. The pattern of placement and wheel size will affect directions and pace of turn. 'Cogs' are added to the 'wheels' by sticking strips of corrugated cardboard around the rims of the jar lids.

Group 4
The fourth group has been given the task of turning what has been learned from the record books of Caunton village school into a play. They are assigned to the reading corner which has temporarily, by judicious use of cardboard, silver paper, paint, cut-out lettering, been converted into a time machine. The 'time' is to be 1861. The play is to be based in fact on the story-lines constructed from the pupils' exploration of the record books. Rehearsals are to be completed; then the finished play is to be taped as if it were a radio broadcast.

Group 5
For this group there is a reversion to the water-wheel theme. Their task is to think of how a windmill works (a diagram is provided). The sails of the windmill turn cogs which in turn turn the millstones. The pupils are asked: can you work out a way to make your *water* wheel fit a model with cogs to turn grindstones? Once a cog is fitted to the water wheel the task is to fit *another* cog to make the machine turn in a different direction. Also, pupils have to work out, using cogs, how to make the machine turn in the *opposite* direction.

The tasks are pre-planned, assigned quickly with all equipment to hand, and the pupils get on immediately. Task orientation is very high. The teacher monitors immediately and constantly. The observer was not able to hear the rapid interchanges between teacher and pupils as she moves round; but he moved into one pupil group and used a dictaphone to record conversation in progress. It is probably typical of the work going on in the rest of the room. The following is an extract from the recording.

Recorded extract of group 1 at work

P.1. Find the area of the tower.

P.2. . . . I know. It's 10 × 8 cms. 10 × 8 is 80. So it's 80 cm square.

P.3. Then what will the area of the windows be? One centimetre square.

P.2. Yes. [They shelve this to read further instructions and to draw a scale diagram. They return to the area question.]

P.2. It's 80.

P.4. But there's 6 and 8 and 10.

P.3. Look, Molly, 10 × 8 = 80 and then times 6. [They start to work it out.]

P.2. 10 add 8 add 6 is . . .

P.1. It's *times*, Molly.

P.2. Oh, yes!

P.3. 10 × 8 = 80; the 8 sixes are . . .

P.1. I don't get that . . .

P.2. 6 × 8 = 48 times 10

P.3. That's wrong. We're not working it out right. We're making it too hard.

P.4. Mrs B. said only multiply *two* sides, didn't she?

P.1. Yes.

P.2. So 10 × 8 is 80, but you've got to take out the windows. That 1 cm^2.

P.3. Let's make a drawing. [They make a scale drawing and decide to put the result under an acetate sheet ruled with centimetre squares.]

P.2. But some of the squares are not whole squares because the sides slope in.

T. [Asks how the pupils are getting on. They explain the problem]. Think about your windmill shape. You can find the area of a square or rectangle. Using the acetate ruled sheet is a good idea. Now put the two ideas together. [Later: the pupils have cut up the scale drawing thus:

Figure 2.2

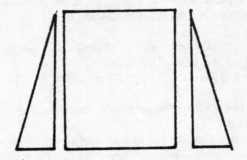

By experiment they have discovered that two triangles make a rectangle.]

Figure 2.3

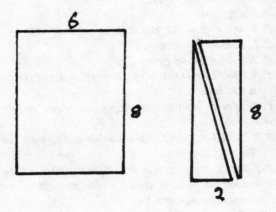

P.1. So we've got 8 × 6 = 48.
P.3. Yes, and 2 × 8 = 16. That's . . .
P.4. 64.
T. Sixty-four what?
P.2. Centimetres.
T. What kind of centimetres?
P.2. Square centimetres.

Just before the bell, the pupils pack equipment away sensibly. Lunch is a scratch affair, a sandwich and a cup of coffee consumed partly in the staffroom and partly back in class. During this time the observer talked to the teacher, eliciting a number of descriptions of her work. It emerged that these pupils have been taught study skills from an early age. The teacher's fundamental philosophy is that learning depends on pupil relations. She believes strongly in each pupil's individuality and in exploiting it; but they have, too, to learn to work together and learn together. If the relationships are right then learning tends to follow. She does, however, acknowledge the place of the teacher in successful learning: it is the teacher who asks the all-important 'why?' questions which lead to exploration. But she sees teaching as a balance between science and art. The science of teaching allows one to scrutinise and analyse the world around us. The art comes into its own at the face-to-face level.

After lunch, the teacher presents the class with a choice. They can either get on with the group-work tasks, or form an audience for the play, prepared by group 4, which is performed 'live'. Initially, some pupils opt out of the play; but as the props are set up they all drift quietly into the main body of the classroom. The teacher tacitly accepts this change of decision.

The pupils have compiled this play by reconstructing events in the log of Caunton School. They have adopted the names and personalities of real characters from the log. By using pictorial sources they have reconstructed the life and looks of the time.

The form of the play is that of an acted narrative. A fairly fluent girl reads the narrator's part; and the others have small memorised parts. The group has worked out the narrative, actions and dialogue for itself. The text was written last week, and had been rehearsed before lunch.

Set in the school and local village, this is the story of a child's school life and incidents such as falling sick. Most of the writing seems to have been done by one pupil; but six are involved in acting and they rope in an ancillary helper who is present to act with them. The play is performed with confidence; and the narrator's part contains a wealth of historical detail. It sets the atmosphere of the harshness of the times well, and captures the rapt attention of the audience. A long discussion follows. The discussion proceeds quickly and wherever possible the following account of it records the teacher's questions verbatim and the gist of the pupil's answers. Most pupils take part and none is allowed to dominate.

T. *What did you learn about Caunton School in 1861?*
   (Children sit on benches)
   (It was very strict)

T. *What did you think of the head?*
   (He was cruel)

T. *Why was he cruel?*
   (He caned people often)
   (He had two canes)

T. *Why did he visit the pupils' homes?*
   (To see if the pupil was all right)
   (To make sure he was really ill)

T. *How long would the pupil have been ill with scarlet fever?*
   (Two weeks)
   (Probably longer)

T. *What would have added to the problems of the illness?*
   (Poor food)
   (Dirty conditions)
   (Polluted water)

T. *How did the water get polluted?*
   (Because there were fish in it)
   (Because animals went in it)
   (People walked through it)

T. *Tell me about the mother's dress.*
   (Dirty)
   (Shawl)
   (Long dress)
   (Bonnet)

T. *Samuel Reynolds Hole was mentioned; who was he?*
   (He lived in the village)
   (He was the vicar)
   (He was also the squire)

T. *A shilling was mentioned; what's a shilling?*
   (Ten pence)
   (Five pence)

T. *Why did they need a shilling for the doctor?*
   (Incorrect response about the vicar)

T. *All right, why was it the vicar who gave the shilling?*
   (Because he was the Son of God)

T. *Let's go back to Samuel Hole — why pay the doctor?*
   (No answer)

T. *Do your parents pay?*
   (No)

T. So what's changed?
(Pupils talk about the NHS)
T. So why was sickness Samuel Hole's business?
(He was the squire)
(He was paying back his vicar's tithe)
T. What does being a squire mean?
(A sort of leader)
T. Where did the squire live?
(Near the school)
(In the Manor House)
T. What was the Manor House surrounded by?
(Roads)
(Fields)
T. Who worked in the fields?
(Labourers)
T. Who did they work for?
(The squire)
T. Right, there are some clues. Can you piece together the story?
(He feels guilty)
(He gets money from them so feels he has to give something back)
T. Who's the most important person in this school?
(The head)
T. Think of the squire like that: the head of the village. So if you're in charge of people what do you feel?
(If someone works hard for his boss, he — the boss — doesn't have to do much)
T. How would you feel about the people who worked for you?
(Kind)
(Caring)
T. So what Leigh is saying is not only is the squire a leader, he ought to feel care for people. Now the man who just painted our classroom used to work for the Hole family, and he said to me: 'Major Hole was a fine man.' Our caretaker used to work there too, and he said the family took care of its workers. In the play what games were mentioned?
(Marbles)
T. And what was 'the workhouse'?
(Pupil explains, giving an illustration from Oliver Twist)
T. That links back to Hole's Brewery. That building used to be the workhouse.

At this point the pupils begin a spontaneous conversation which ends by their asking the teacher for a repeat of the play. She agrees and says that this time the audience's job is to count the number of genuine contemporary touches which reflect life in the Victorian era; and also to spot omissions.

The performers prepare to repeat the play, while the teacher gives advice to the pupil narrator on how to improve her performance. Afterwards:

> *T. What authentic details did you spot?*
> *(metal ruler*
> *slate pencils*
> *big black boots*
> *girls with collars*
> *different age pupils in one class*
> *no electric lights*
> *no gas*
> *no wall displays*
> *no blinds*
> *no drawing pins*
> *windows too high to see out)*

The afternoon break is moments away and the teacher urges the pupils back into groups ready to finish the group-work tasks in the last session of the day.

A more rounded view

So far we have been able to look at the topic work in progress at Roseborough school through three sets of eyes: the head's, the class teacher's and the case-study worker's. In research terms it is this cross-checking of perceptions which validates the case study. There is indeed a consistency about the scene presented; but, as in daily life, each new account of the same phenomenon adds a fresh dimension and increases its vitality.

The case-study worker's account suffers from the usual problems of this kind of research. He is physically incapable of noting every detail of every child's activity simultaneously. So the account is selective in two ways. For some of the time he concentrates on an individual pupil or a group of pupils, so that the part has to represent the whole. Sometimes he has to make judgements about the relative importance of a set or sequence of classroom events, so that he can concentrate on describing what he sees as the most salient events.

In order to overcome these potential areas of bias in the observations the case-study worker observed lessons on a number of occasions stretching over a couple of months. As well as the freehand accounts he adopted other, more systematic, methods for collecting data about life in the classroom studied. The narrative account, taken back to base, analysed and reflected upon, might raise questions in his mind. How much time did the pupils actually spend on task? What was the balance between whole-class teaching and group work? The teacher asked a lot of questions — to what extent were these open or closed, cognitively demanding or simple matters of fact? To answer these questions other periods of observation might be planned specifically to observe the use made of particular teaching strategies. In this way a more rounded view of the whole learning experience of the pupil could be compiled.

To gain this rounded view with reference to the present case, a possible starting point would be to return to Mrs Byrd's own account of her classroom practice given in an earlier section of this chapter (*Mrs Byrd, year-group leader and class teacher*). The reader might care to refresh his or her memory of the section at this point. Close scrutiny of this section would reveal the teacher's intentions for learning, and these can be summarised as follows.

The underlying philosophy or rationale of this classroom is that children should be acquiring certain methods and skills of thinking: to make deductions, to analyse objects and situations and to draw sensible conclusions based on this analysis. In order to achieve these ends the children are asked to work in groups, where discussion takes place both with and without the teacher, and where peers learn with and from each other. This learning is active: the youngsters 'do not just listen'. Specific learning experiences are provided by the teacher, and her role is adapted, to facilitate this kind of learning around the theme, in this case 'man the farmer and settler'.

Having identified these intentions, the case-study worker might scrutinise his lesson accounts and more systematic data to see to what extent and in what ways these intentions are fulfilled. An earlier section in this chapter (*A lesson in progress*) contained a complete account of a lesson in progress. The reader might care to re-read this section, assessing for himself the match or mismatch between practice and intentions. In the paragraphs that follow we have culled snippets from other case-studied lessons taught by Mrs Byrd and used them to illustrate the approach described.

The children in Mrs Byrd's class were expected to deduce, analyse and draw conclusions. A close examination of the case-study data revealed that this demand was made often, and in a variety of ways. Here, for example, is the text of a work-card:

> *Be history detectives.*
> *Look at the 1799 map of Caunton village.*
> *Compare it with the 1968 map.*
> *How many river crossings were there in 1799?*
> *How many are marked on the modern map?*
> *How were these crossings marked in 1799? In 1968?*
> *What sort of crossings were they in 1799?*
> *How did they differ in 1968?*
> *(and so on)*

The teacher's questions reflected a similar approach. This is a sample section of dialogue taken verbatim from a case-study account.

Mrs B. Have you tried putting the two maps together? What's the
   first thing you notice?
P. There are more houses now.
Mrs B. What else have you spotted?
P. More roads.
P. The fields are bigger now.
P. The river's changed.
Mrs B. How?
P. It's straightened.
P. And there are more trees in 1968 than there were in 1799.
Mrs B. That's important. The colours on the map give that away.
   Why should that be?
P. They hold the soil together.
P. They look good.
Mrs B. Yes, they prevent soil erosion. And *where* are they planted?
P. Round the Manor House.
Mrs B. So who might have planted them?
P. Samuel Hole, the squire.
Mrs B. If the people who lived on the Manor and owned the estate
   put the trees there in 1799, how would it have helped them?
P. (speculates incorrectly)
Mrs B. How did these people farm?
P. In small fields.

Mrs B. So how would trees help?
P. They would mark out the field edges . . .

In this dialogue the children are analysing, deducing and drawing conclusions. They are doing this in a small group with the teacher. Mrs Byrd's intention is for such learning groups to function without her presence, too, and for learning to proceed along similar lines even among these young pupils. Some teachers would be dubious about whether this could happen, perhaps. The next extract from the worker's case-notes will allow them to judge for themselves. An unsupervised group is comparing maps of Caunton village in 1799 and 1968:

P.1. It looks as if the river should be there [1968 map].
P.2. Not on my map [1799] it doesn't.
P.3. I think it's changed the shape, look, there.
P.4. The farmland's changed, too. There isn't so much farmland.
P.1. Don't forget what Mrs Byrd says: round every farm is usually
*   three fields.*
P.3. Yeah.
P.2. So they can swap the crops.
P.3. But on here there isn't [i.e. the 1968 map] . . .
P.5. Hey, look. On this [1799] map they didn't know the spring,
*   'cos the spring's here.*
P.2. Yes, and that field isn't there is it?
P.4. These two [1799 hedges] are a bit straighter than these [1968],
*   aren't they?*
P.3. They've got lots of fields [in 1799].
P.1. We're meant to be looking at the river crossing.
P.2. The bumps in it are smaller [in 1968].
P.4. The river now is longer and more straighter.
P.1. Yeah. It's the same with these roads. Look.

The organisation of the class into working groups, so much a part of this teacher's style of working, is well illustrated by these extracts from the caseworker's notes. They relate to two different lessons.

To understand these lesson accounts one needs to know how the lessons are organised. Mrs Byrd usually begins with a few minutes of whole-class instruction — this may be very brief. The work is carried out in groups. The teacher monitors constantly. Each group has a separate task. Though all pupils will be following the same scheme of work it may be that only some groups will be occupied in scheme-related work at any given time; others may be doing maths or some other activity, for the teacher's approach is characterised by flexibility.

My first task today is to record the tasks in progress in each group. These are as follows:

Group 1
Pupils have a yoke and leather fittings from the horse-trappings from an old plough or farm cart. They know more or less what the objects are but are analysing them according to the 'classification of man-made objects' proforma which the teacher has provided. This consists of a series of questions about the nature of the object or material. The work relates to old farming methods in their village survey, the survey which is underpinning all this section of their topic work.

Group 2
This is the group which was comparing the 1799 with 1968 maps of the village. They have completed their preliminary discussions and are now answering questions on specially prepared work-cards.

Group 3
The third group is experimenting with wind power, making paper sails for windmills using various designs. The ancillary helper is assisting them to test the designs outdoors.

Group 4
The theme here is historical records and pupils have
(a) a Banda copy of the local census returns
(b) *Sunday at home*: a massive leather-bound book dated 1874.
The group is working from a set of teacher-made work-cards, 'History from records at the time'. The specific task is to look at the pictures in the book and to discover differences between the clothes of 1874 and those of the 1980s.

Group 5
The last group is using a Banda sheet of questions about the village survey visit they had just undertaken. They are writing answers in rough prior to putting them into record books.

The teacher's intentions are to provide deductive learning experiences for pupils in groups, to make learning active and to facilitate this kind of classroom experience. The case-notes already quoted illustrate how this works.

But the case-study worker might also wish to stand outside the situation a little and become more systematic in his observations. For example, there can be little doubt that deductive and analytical tasks are set in Mrs Byrd's lessons and that she organises groups in the way she claims to. From the dialogue of pupil–pupil conversations it is clear that these youngsters can get on unsupervised and carry out quite difficult tasks. But how much or how little of their time is spent in this way? Is concentration just a flash-in-the-pan affair? The case-study worker decided to see just how dedicated to the task the youngsters were by using a time on task measure. To use this, each child is observed for a period (say, 30 seconds). During this period the observer uses a stopwatch to calculate how many seconds are spent working on the task. The same process is repeated for each child in turn. The total number of seconds worked by each pupil is added up, and is expressed as a percentage of total observation time. This gives a simple but generally reliable measure of time on task during a lesson. Experiments with this technique have shown that student-teachers may achieve time-on-task ratings of anything between 10 per cent and 90 per cent; and that experienced teachers probably average in the range 60–65 per cent. In Mrs Byrd's lesson the time on task by pupils was 77.7 per cent. At the time when the measure was taken the pupils were working in five groups. A small unsupervised group achieved 100 per cent time on task; a group supervised by an ancillary helper achieved 92 per cent; another unsupervised group scored 89 per cent; a group supervised by the teacher initially and then working alone scored 64 per cent; and the fifth, unsupervised, group spent 48 per cent of its time on task. Thus the achievement of the teacher's intention and the case-study worker's impression of a class busily employed in purposeful task-related activity were strongly supported by a systematic and objective measurement.

What has been reported so far has enabled us to see that the teacher's goal of deductive learning in groups is a fact of life in this classroom. Already enough has been said to show that much learning is being done, including discussing; and that her intentions about providing specific learning experiences in which the teacher facilitates these kinds of activity are consistently fulfilled over a period of time. Our case-studied lessons, then, can be used to illustrate the degree of matching between intentions and practice, which in Mrs Byrd's case is very high. They can also be used to identify and illustrate teaching strategies and techniques, and to exemplify these. Above all, these case studies of heads and teachers discussing their work, and the lesson accounts, can help us to isolate for scrutiny specific problem areas and examine a range of solutions to them in a practical context.

The case described in this chapter has been used primarily to show the reader how case-study data can be collected and used. This case has itself raised some problem areas or issues in topic-work teaching, despite the fact that the effectiveness of the practice described can hardly be doubted.

These issues are best formulated as questions, for example:

What should be the overall aims and intentions for a school's topic work?

What information, social and practical skills and concepts should pupils be learning?

How does this learning progress during the primary years?

What teaching strategies and methods are most suited to teaching this material?

What are the criteria for judging learning success?

How can learning be effectively monitored and recorded?

How can an individual teacher identify, reflect upon and refine the skills he/she will need to carry out the teaching role with increasing effectiveness?

In the present case, most of these issues have been clearly identified and thoughtfully tackled in the school already. Not all schools have progressed this far in reviewing their topic-work provision. Roseborough's solutions may not work in different locations — in urban sprawls or the isolated rural school, in schools with a different staff ethos or where staff talents are biased in other directions.

We used Roseborough, and other schools in our study, not to provide definitive answers but to point up these problems and issues. We used case-study accounts of Roseborough's solutions, and of those in other schools, to suggest possible lines of approach to these issues — issues common across the profession.

The chapter which follows looks at some of the major issues in topic-work teaching as they were revealed to us by teachers and heads in our study. Thereafter, the remainder of the book seeks to come to grips with these issues, using extracts from our collected case-study data to illustrate both the problems themselves and some possible solutions.

At no time have we set out to provide a blueprint for effective topic work or a 'follow the recipe for instant success' approach. Rather, we have sought to exemplify how thoughtful professionals have approached their work and to encourage a way of thinking about the subject. Every teacher, every pupil, every classroom and every school has a unique quality. That uniqueness is valuable; and what is sought is the kind of flexibility which can adapt and improvise, can blend its own insights into an eclectic solution to an individual problem. In short, we are aiming at thinking teachers.

3

Issues from Cases: an Overview

FOUR MAJOR ISSUES

The previous chapter has served to provide an example of how case-study data were collected, and what kinds of information became available using this method. We have seen how caseworkers' reports, interviews with head teachers and teachers, classroom observations of both narrative and systematic varieties, and the written reactions of all the parties involved to the impressions of others were combined to form a 'data bank' of evidence about the ways in which schools and classrooms in the study functioned. These data were augmented by interviews with pupils about their reactions to topic work, by collected samples of pupils' work and by photographs of classrooms and pupils at work. Examples of these data have been used to describe topic work in progress in one school, Roseborough.

In all, seven case-study workers collected information about twenty teachers in eight schools across three counties where LEA advisers felt that the work in progress was particularly interesting. In addition, eleven teachers in six other schools undertook carefully structured case studies of their own work, making a total of 31 case studies in all. None of these schools or teachers should be described as 'typical' — the epithet is meaningless in a case-study context. Each was unique. But we discovered that they shared *common problems and issues* about topic-work teaching and sometimes they shared *common elements* in their solutions to these issues. Between them, they also provided an informed *variety of solutions*. It became our conviction that providing some mechanism for pooling this wide-ranging professional expertise, for communicating the insights from the 'data bank' back to its contributors, and for making these insights available to the wider profession, was the major role that we as researcher-developers had to play.

If this were a research report of the case-study activity we should follow a description of our case-study methodology by setting out each case in turn. Subsequently, we should analyse the critical points to emerge, and we would try to draw some generalisable conclusions about how topic work is taught or might be improved. But this is not a report of 'pure research' and our function at all stages of the enquiry was primarily to examine the practical teaching implications and in-service training potential of the case studies.

For this reason, we can operate a developer's licence in dealing with our material, and can present it in a way and in an order more suited to the needs of the practising teacher. This chapter, therefore, leaves aside the sequential examination of each case, and looks in a more informal way at the emergent issues. The rest of the book then returns to the 'data bank' of cases to illustrate the issues in depth, and to exemplify some possible solutions to them.

Almost all the issues to emerge from our cases fell under one of four major headings.

MANAGING TOPIC WORK

The first major issue was that of *managing topic work*, with the emphasis on the kind of management which takes place at school level. This issue would be highlighted in the kinds of case-study extracts which follow.

First, we can eavesdrop on a conversation between the four year-group leaders who comprise the middle management structure of an 8–12 middle school in a difficult suburban environment:

Case-study worker. Between you, you've raised the issue of managing learning. How do you plan for topic work — I don't mean lesson preparation — but does this fortnightly year-group leaders' meeting act as a vehicle for your curriculum planning?
Year 3 leader. Everything is done independently.
Year 2 leader. Bush telegraph is the method . . . we're not consciously guided in our choice by what the first year have done or what the third year will do after. If it happens to fit in that's marvellous, but it's not the criterion by which we choose . . .
Year 4 leader. Year 3 may do a topic on water or fire; but it

65

wouldn't make any difference to me. I could even do the same title if I wished.

Two teachers in a medium-size primary school in the small market town of Padkey were studied by a case-study worker, who was informed by the head that, while he had reviewed provision of numeracy and literacy for his pupils, he had not yet been in post long enough to tackle the topic curriculum. The resulting very different intentions of the two teachers for topic work are described in the worker's notes:

Mrs Atkin reported spending between 25% and 50% of her time on topic work; while Mr Bedlow spent between 10% and 25% . . . Mr Bedlow thought of topic work as a thematic approach within a single discipline. His children were seen to work individually or in pairs to follow a line of (scientific) enquiry, but then to come together as a class to discuss the results and findings . . . Mrs Atkin saw the topic as the largest single element on the timetable, as interdisciplinary, and as not precluding a good deal of whole-class work . . . Mr Bedlow's children worked closely to questions on a work-card, Mrs Atkin's exercised some degree of choice and initiative in pursuing individual (historical) enquiries.

As well as planning procedures and decisions about such crucial questions as how much time should be occupied by this work, management issues include those which delineate the scope of the curriculum and the kinds of progress children make in tackling it. These questions are hinted at in the following extracts. Here a head teacher of a small rural primary school is talking to the case-study worker:

CSW. How has the curriculum changed since you came to this school?

Head. It's sort of changed incidentally, I suppose, in that the staff get on very well with each other. We all share similar interests and ages; and we get on socially as well as in school. Therefore, changes in policy and curriculum have happened as a matter of course. We have said 'We're not happy with it; how can we make it better?' Mrs G. told me when I first came that she didn't know what environmental studies was — yet she was doing it, following an environmental studies policy of her own . . . In fact, we've got a meeting tonight to discuss next term's topic and we sit around with an initial idea.

CSW. How did you think of this idea?
Head. It happens.

On the question of monitoring and recording progress one teacher of a fourth-year class in a middle school remarked:

How do I assess pupils' work in topic lessons? By effort and achievement. Effort and progress are easily recognised. Achievement is measured by one's expectation of standards attainable by the individual child. I do not keep written records of children's topic work.

A further management question concerns the relationship between work labelled 'topic' and other curriculum areas: literacy, numeracy, science, or the creative or aesthetic arts. Once more, a quotation from a case study puts the issue into a form in which it is open to considerable debate; and the important problem of how traditional subjects integrate into topic work is considered.

Notes from the caseworker's interview with a head teacher

Head. We have a horizontal structure. A year co-ordinator for each year. The year co-ordinators devise the year programmes. Not quite true to say mornings are spent on basics and afternoons on topic. As pupils progress up the school there is more specialisation, e.g. French in year 3 and Technical Drawing in year 4. Also afternoons are partly absorbed in PE, music, etc.

CSW. What is the relationship between formal curriculum (language, maths, subject areas) and the topic work in formal curriculum?

Head. Basic subjects, especially language, come into all work. The answer depends on the actual themes themselves. In topic, it is important not to contrive connections between subjects and themes. Conversely, themes must relate, not be totally watertight. But interdisciplinary themes show connections naturally between, say, science and cookery; and this connection is made through the skills of the teacher.

CSW. [Recaps on three points: interdisciplinary nature of topic work; use of technical language, e.g. in science; topic implies some problem-solving]

Head. [Agrees he has said these things.]
But what is important is the formulation of aims of the work. There are taboos — e.g. just copying. Though pupils are

*encouraged to use books for enjoyment, imagination, informa-
tion. Pupils get enthusiastic and take topic work home, they do
it in wet play-times and so on. [CSW comments: we began to talk
about aims and hinted at several. But in fact this discussion hardly
got off the ground. Is there more to be said?]*

*CSW. You said that across the four year groups the pupils have very
different experiences because of differences in staff approaches.
Can you elaborate?*

*Head. One important duty of a head is to gather the right staff, to
get a balance, and (this is crucial) to place the staff so as to
provide a progression for the pupils.*

In year 1 the essential element is to make the pupils secure.

*In year 2 the teachers get a great deal of oral work to stretch their
language work and this is helped by a gifted teacher of drama.
He suggests, poses questions, etc.*

*In year 3 there is a bit of specialisation; concrete experiences are
put on paper; work is a bit more formal.*

*In year 4 you are looking over your shoulder at the secondary
schools. There they face 'lectures'. We help pupils to cope by
showing them* how *to learn and study.*

In this chapter we have intentionally put the emphasis on quotations from cases which express doubt, enquiry and somewhat
negative approaches, for it is precisely through such self-scrutiny
and soul-searching that issues become crystallised. It is a legitimate
process through which we all need to go. The chapters which follow
will contrast with this approach by concentrating on experiments,
ideas and proven methodologies. For the moment, however, this
slightly pessimistic string of extracts has helped to formulate the
management issues in topic work, and the time is now opportune to
extrapolate and list these in a more orderly way. By using a question
format we shall be able to explore this group of issues more
systematically in subsequent chapters. The management issues,
then, emerge as follows.

Questions about curriculum management in topic work

Questions of policy

Has the school an agreed policy for topic teaching?

Is it clearly laid down?

Is it accessible to, and known by, all staff?

By what mechanism does the head ensure that staff abide by its principles?

What kinds of consultation went into its formulation?

Is it reviewed regularly?

Do staff meet regularly to this end?

Questions of curriculum balance and monitoring

Who ensures that a child's curriculum is balanced?

Across each school year? Across a school career?

How is this achieved?

Who monitors that the work is covered by the teachers?

How does the monitoring take place?

Questions of school management structure

Which staff have special responsibility for implementing topic-work policy? Head? Deputy? Year leaders? Scale-post holders?

What are their respective roles? Responsibilities? Powers?

When do they meet?

Who chairs the meetings?

What form do the meetings take?

Is there a proper agenda?

Questions of intention, content, skills and integration

Are there clear sets of aims and intentions for topic work?

Are there clear guidelines about the practical and social skills the pupils need to acquire?

Are there sets of concepts identified as necessary for learning?

Is a certain content regarded as essential?

Are staff aware of these agreed skills, concepts and data?

Are topic titles selected at school level? How? By whom? On what criteria?

How are decisions made about the duration of topics? When they should start and finish?

What criteria are used for deciding which work is taught through integrated approaches? Through themes? In subject blocks?

How does topic work relate to work done in basic subjects? In other areas of the curriculum?

Questions of progression

How do staff monitor what the children have learned?

How do they record the progress pupils have made?

Are these monitoring and recording strategies sufficiently flexible to cope with all facets of the pupils' learning?

Questions of professional development and accountability

How do teachers keep up to date with thinking in this field?

Do they attend courses?

How are staff selected for courses?

Is the professional development of each individual teacher monitored? By whom? How?

Do teachers evaluate their *own* work? How?

Is there a clear rationale about what constitutes successful topic work?

Is this applied regularly to work in progress? When? By whom?

Who is responsible for amendments of policy or improvements in practice?

Does the school communicate its topic-work policies to parents? To other interested parties: advisers, the infant school, the comprehensive school? When? How?

Does it foster co-operation with other interested outsiders: in industry, in the public services, from parents?

These are the kinds of questions about managing topic work which are implicit and explicit in the case-study data and which are brought to the surface by careful scrutiny of what the participant teachers, heads and research workers have to say about real schools and real pupils. We have come to believe that these questions have a generalisable quality, that they are shared by the profession as a whole. Our experiments in in-service training and our questionnaire researches, both described elsewhere in this book, have confirmed this view. In the same way, there are other major issues besides the management one, and it is to the second of these that we now turn.

PREPARING A TOPIC

We can now move on to the point where a teacher moves out of the staffroom and into the classroom. How does essential lesson-preparation take place and with what processes is it concerned? This preparation issue was the second of the four major issues to emerge from the case-study data.

Inevitably, the four major issues interweave and overlap to some extent in their scope. In this case it seems entirely appropriate, from the evidence, to begin with the teacher's aims for topic lessons, in other words with his or her view of what he/she is hoping to achieve. As we have seen in the foregoing section, a school may adopt a common policy for this curriculum area and may spell out some global intentions for all staff. Here, the question is, on the one hand, about how those intentions are translated into course aims and objectives by individual teachers, and on the other about what happens in schools where no such policy or public set of intentions exists.

The process of thinking analytically about teaching is one which, until recently, has been poorly handled at the initial training level, and often not tackled at all for in-service practitioners. Those concerned with in-service work all too frequently take one or other of two unhelpful views. Either they see self-analysis as an unnecessary practice to cultivate since 'experienced teachers do it anyway', or they regard it as the 'precious ramblings of woolly academics in education departments'. At the initial training level there is a widespread view that 'practical teaching is an intuitive skill' and hence, by definition apparently, one does not need to reflect upon it. We were not altogether surprised in our case-study data, therefore, to discover that some of even the most dynamic teachers appeared not to have come to any clear statement of intent about why they were teaching a particular topic in a particular way, or that their rationale was somewhat restricted. This piece of question and response is not untypical:

CSW. In topic work are there overall sets of aims agreed at school level?
4th-year teacher. No.

71

CSW. Do you formulate your own aims?
4th-year teacher. Yes.
CSW. What are they and why have you selected them?
4th-year teacher. Strong emphasis is placed on the children learning
  facts to gain understanding. I believe that real understanding of
  a subject can only be acquired when certain basic facts are
  learned, including the vocabulary associated with that subject
  . . . I'm not interested in the so-called skills approach. I'm more
  concerned that these pupils need to work on, and know, informa-
  tion. I'm concerned with good presentation and that they know
  how to compose a piece of writing.

This almost antediluvian statement presents a point of view which
was much more restricted than the caseworker's impressions of what
was achieved by the lessons of this most able teacher; but it does
raise the critical question of how teachers formulate intentions for
lessons or a series of lessons, and what those intentions are. In the
following extract a headmistress of a three-teacher all-age primary
school talks to the caseworker about her intentions. One of the
features of this response to the question about aims and purpose in
topic work is its *struggle* after a rationale, though the words come
from a highly experienced and respected professional:

To teach the children. I suppose this is a philosophy, really. To teach
the children to cope with society, the society they are going into, the
political and technological world they are going into. I'm not so
concerned with teaching the principles of flight or teaching them
how a coloured picture is made. What I am concerned with is
teaching the children where they can obtain information from, so
that when they leave the confines of a 90-place primary school and
enter the jungle of the town up the road, the even bigger jungle of
adulthood and unemployment, they can find things out and go to the
library; they can look in an index, they can use encyclopaedias, they
can go to the museum to get help that way, the archives if they want
to. They can be taught all these things and can pick out the sources
of information.
  I am not actually saying that I am doing a 'television topic' or my
main aim is to teach the children about how colour is produced.
These are incidental aims. They are all part and parcel of topic
work, and they are all basic aims within the topic. Yes, I do hope
to be able to teach the children about colour on television and how
we see pictures, because I think that's interesting. But the main aim

is that we teach children how to use books, how to précis what they see, how to write down the information, how to use it, how to be more fluent — talking as well. We do a lot of cassette work, interviewing, and the children interview each other . . . A lot of our work is in interviewing and using cassettes and going out to interview people: teaching children to talk to other people. I mean, that's an important aim, and it's not just in topic work. That's the philosophy. It's all in the big melting-pot.

These two extracts, then, show the striving towards a set of classroom intentions. Some schools and some teachers have progressed further along this road than the authors of the two quotations; and their solutions to the question of aims and objectives will be examined later. For the moment we continue to concentrate on those planning areas where there are obvious difficulties for some teachers and, of these, the business of choosing a topic title is often tackled in no very systematic way. Two brief extracts from individual cases exemplify this issue.

As soon as the schools programme becomes available I look to see if there's anything useful coming up on television next term. Then I wait until the first programme and the pupils watch it. If it goes down well and looks promising then we build our topic round it.

Sometimes one of us might come to school and say: 'Oh, I was inspired last night and thought about this.' Or perhaps Junior Education or Child Education magazine might have something that sparks us off. We might find something in next year's programmes for schools on TV that we think might be interesting. I don't think we've ever adopted any topic in the time I've been here that we haven't all been able to get enthusiastic about in some way. I think when someone suggests something that you're not particularly keen on, we will say: 'Oh dear, I don't know if I could do that . . .' It is quite easy when there's only a small number of us . . . we can get together over coffee any old time of day and reach a consensus. Well, I came in with the idea, just before Christmas, of doing 'entertainment'. We tossed the idea over and decided after various discussions it was too broad an area and we narrowed it down to just 'television'. And it works like that.

It doesn't seem to have occurred to these teachers that perhaps there are *educational* reasons why some topics should be covered

rather than other, or that staff preference and the immediate convenience of available resources might be minor rather than major
reasons for adopting a particular segment of curriculum content
along with its associated skills and concepts, and for leaving aside
others. In the second quotation all sorts of questions are begged
about the suitability of a particular topic title for all pupils in an all-
through primary. There may be a fallacy in the view that the change
of title from 'entertainment' to 'television' is necessarily a narrow-
ing or limiting process. The medium of television might feature to
some degree in a topic about entertainment; but as a topic in its own
right it demands to be explored, perhaps, along such paths as
technology and production techniques that would not necessarily
have impinged on the entertainment angle.

Enough has been said, then, in this section to open up two
avenues of enquiry under the major issue of preparation for topic
work: finding a rationale and choosing a topic. Some further
preparation issues are raised in the following case-study extract,
which deals with the practical matter of the readiness of teacher and
pupils to tackle a given topic.

*If the topics fit in with a school's TV or radio programme I use the
programme notes as well as reference books and other reference
material from our (school) resources centre. Teaching method
varies. Some topics are more suitable for class lessons. A recent
study of the life cycle of butterflies and moths was largely done from
individual work-cards, though, using microscopes. I gather a project
collection of books from the County Library, and some from the
school library. Also: wall pictures and maps from the resources
centre; globes; time-charts (if relevant); filmstrips, slides, cassettes;
duplicated sheets of diagrams, pictures or questionnaires, work-
cards for various levels of ability; newspaper cuttings. In the class
I display the book collections, put up the wall-charts and letter
headings, and provide trays for work-cards and duplicate sheets. I
make one topic folder for each child; and then collect together art
and craft materials — paper, card, glue, paint, clay. I think about
it all over several weeks, and add ideas as I come across them.*

This description of preparation for topic teaching is essentially a
practical one. It is extremely detailed about the question of resources
and their availability, it hints at the use of display as a teaching
medium, it takes into account differential provision for pupils of
varying abilities, and it implies the value of the child's work in the

provision of a topic folder. It doesn't tackle questions about progression in the direction and difficulty of the work or about the knowledge, skills or concepts to be learned. It does suggest, in the first sentence, some learning at the teacher's own level; and the duration of such preparation is discussed. This extract is not unlike many others in the case studies except in one particular: unlike many, this teacher does not apparently plan the topic content on a flow diagram or planning web (this method will be examined in some detail in a later chapter).

At this point, then, it is probably opportune to summarise the planning issue in a series or questions, exactly as we did earlier in the chapter with the main issue of managing topic work. Questions about planning might include:

Questions about preparation for topic teaching

Questions about intentions and objectives

As a classroom teacher, what are your aims, intentions and objectives for topic teaching?

How do you decide upon these for any given topic?

Do you know precisely the main

   items of knowledge
   practical and social skills
   concepts and ideas

you hope to impart through any given topic?

Questions about planning procedures

Do you have a systematic approach to preparation, an order in which you prepare yourself, your resources, your pupils and the classroom?

Do you commit your planning to paper?

How long would you expect to spend in preparation for an unfamiliar topic?

When is this preparation carried out?

Do you commit this planning to paper?

Do you pass your plans to anyone else for comment?

Do you use the plans again for other classes, or destroy them when the topic is over?

Questions of resources and teaching method

In planning, do you look to resources and resource people beyond the school gates — the teachers' centre, potential speakers, places to visit, parents?

How do you decide upon the most appropriate teaching methods for any given topic? For each topic lesson?

Questions of classroom organisation

What account do you take, in planning, of what pupils already know? How do you find this out?

Is your classroom orderly?

Do pupils know where basic resources and pieces of equipment are?

Can they get on without fussing?

Do they have the requisite study skills — adequate reading ability, knowledge of an index, etc.?

If not, is study-skills acquisition built into the topic?

Have you thought ahead to provide suitable alternative activities for the slowest? The most able?

Is everything ready in advance?

Questions of pupil's learning

Have you devised some way(s) of monitoring the extent to which children are acquiring

    the items of knowledge
    the practical and social skills
    the concepts and ideas

you regard as essential or desirable for learning through this topic?

How are you carrying out this monitoring process?

To whom, besides yourself, is this information relevant?

How will it be imparted? When? For what purpose?

A question of criteria

What criteria help you to formulate the choice of a specific topic?

Questions of pupil participation in planning

Do pupils share in this planning? How?

Do they help to choose the topic itself? Areas of interest within it? Methods of working?

These questions indicate the kinds of preparation issues and planning stages through which a teacher needs to work before setting out to teach a topic. Once these have been tackled the scene is set for effective classroom contact with pupils, and it is to this that we turn for the third of our four major issues.

CLASSROOM PROCESSES

We turn our attention now to that most critical of all issues — what happens in the classroom when the teacher is teaching and when the pupils are learning. For convenience we can call these events classroom processes. Our case studies suggested that a number of these were worthy of particular scrutiny because of their central nature to the business of topic teaching. The intention here is to look briefly at these processes one by one, again using case-study extracts to raise questions about them. The emergent questions will be summarised at the end of this section, and some examples of possible methods of rethinking approaches to these processes will be examined in detail later in the book.

Fundamental to the processes of teaching and learning is the question of how pupils are grouped, for this is the context within which these processes function. The dilemma is summed up in this case extract. The speaker is a deputy head of a large suburban all-through primary and the class teacher of a third-year group.

Whole-class teaching is used to introduce the topic and for teaching some study skills, e.g. mapwork. I usually begin and end lessons with the whole class together anyway, and discuss work to be done. When group work is in progress, the more able are ready to move on to further reading and research more rapidly than slower children. Children work in groups for about half the allotted time; sometimes these groups are of mixed ability, sometimes they are really 'sets'. Tasks are often set very formally, with the group's aims very specific, and individual children's separate roles set out.

There are a lot of issues here and it is opportune to spell them out.

First, the dilemma is always one of teaching mode — whether the teacher should control the learning of all pupils at once, or whether youngsters should work alone or in groups. Whole-class teaching is apparently easier to handle, but it thrives on what might be called the myth of simultaneity. It assumes that, because the teacher presents certain information within a given time, all the pupils will acquire an acceptable percentage of it and that the pace of acquisition will not be such as totally to outstrip the slowest or wholly to kill the concentration of the quickest thinkers. It must at least be questioned, and is indeed questionable, whether any of these assumptions are valid.

This view of whole-class teaching wholly ignores the very real question of how to cater for individual differences. In primary classes this is not simply a problem of providing some materials around the given theme which have simplified cognitive demand and some which require advanced thought. Poor readers, non-readers, ultra-competent readers, children who have returned from three weeks' absence with chicken-pox, pupils who have just moved into the area, in short a whole range of individuals, must be given both social security and intellectual stimulation of an appropriate kind.

Nevertheless the extract quoted above certainly puts one positive view of whole-class teaching, which is its role as a medium for pupils' shared experiences; and this theme will be explored further in later chapters.

So, if whole-class teaching has to give way to other forms of learning organisation, the teacher frequently falls back, as here, on group work: a method immediately complicated by the issues of criteria for assigning youngsters to the groups. Ability, friendship, age (in vertically grouped classes), aptitudes, social factors — all these are used by teachers and all will need to be considered in due course.

True individualised learning, where each child is given or negotiates a discrete task appropriate to his immediate needs, is relatively infrequent, which perhaps explains the brevity of teachers' references to it. A class teacher of second-year juniors said: 'Individualised learning is the method I use particularly when I want children to find out things from reference books.'

Be that as it may, classroom processes are not just about the context of learning but about those aspects of teacher behaviour that are labelled 'teaching skills'. They are about effective classroom management; about the ability of the teacher to explain, question and set interesting and demanding tasks; about the teacher's proficiency in providing a variety of learning experiences which pupils see to be valuable. Perhaps these skills are best surveyed by watching a lesson in progress, so let us join a young woman teacher of a third-year class in an 8–12 middle school. The topic is 'Hills' and the youngsters are going, in a few weeks' time, to a field centre in the Peak District to study the phenomenon at first hand. The account of Mrs Cole's lesson, taken from the caseworker's notebook, is as follows:

There are 26 pupils in a box classroom, sitting in pairs, in regular rows. One ventilator stands open but the room is over-warm. The classroom is quite bleak overall: the notice-boards are covered in coloured paper, but are empty of all except four posters from Esso. There is a small book display on the English regions.

1.12 p.m. The teacher begins the lesson by referring in the atlases provided to work done in a previous lesson. She asks a sequence of revision questions (recorded below), each of which was answered by a pupil by consulting the atlas and giving a brief factual response.

Mrs Cole. What do the colours on the map mean?
   What are [sic] the largest chain of hills in England?
   What are [sic] the large chain in Wales called?
   What is the highest Welsh mountain?
   What is the highest English mountain?
   What is the name of the area where Scafell is?
   What are the mountains on the English/Scottish border? . . . [In this extract the list of questions has been curtailed at this point.]
   Right, now turn to page 20 of the atlas — Northern Ireland.
   What is the highest mountain — in Northern Ireland?
   Name two other mountain areas there.
   Very well. Today we're going to put these mountain areas on the map. Have your atlases ready for reference. I'm giving you all a Banda map of Great Britain. On the back of the sheet we're going to make a list of the highest mountains and mountain ranges. Then we'll give each a number. This will become a key. Put your name on the top, left, front of the sheet; write on the back in pencil.

[The map blanks are given out. They are good and clear. Mrs Cole puts the words KEY TO MAP on the board.]

Mrs Cole. Put this title on the back of the Banda map.
   Underline it.

Use a pencil.
Start at the south-west corner. [She demonstrates, writing '1.
DARTMOOR' *on the board.]*
Write that. Then fill in Dartmoor on the map itself by writing the
figure '1'. [She demonstrates and continues to demonstrate with
'2. EXMOOR'.]
Right, that's how we're going to do it, but first we'll make this
list of areas on the back of the Banda map. We'll do that together.
Afterwards you can plot the numbers on the map yourselves.
Near the south coast are the South Downs and North Downs. List
these as 3 and 4. Which range goes up from the Bristol Channel?
Pupil. (reads from the atlas) Mendips.
Mrs Cole. Put that as 5. [This precisely similar procedure is now
followed until a list of twenty hill ranges is listed.]

Looking back over the classroom processes exemplified by this
extract we can readily identify problem areas. The lesson is
excessively repetitious in style. The caseworker formed the impression that 'The children did notice but were extremely tolerant.'
Nevertheless,

When the pupils were set to work alone a queue formed at the
teacher's desk. Some pupils became obscured from the teacher's
vision. Many were restive. It was very airless. Noise level was
moderate until the last five minutes . . . there was some boredom
and frittering . . . the quality of the pupils' maps was variable and
none was terribly good.

There are, then, as one might have suspected, class-management
problems here. Dullness of lessons and inattention by pupils can
rapidly become part of a vicious circle of events. Apart from the
mechanical chore of transferring information from the atlas to the
Banda map, all the work covered in this lesson was a revision of the
previous one in the sequence. Indeed, the whole nature of the task
is open to debate. Was this transfer of information from atlas to
Banda sheet really necessary? What new purpose did it serve? Could
there have been some better way of achieving the same purpose —
a quiz, perhaps, or a treasure hunt with appropriate clues? Was this
repetitious and apparently pointless task just one of a series of
similar tasks?

The task did not require much thought beyond the recall level;
pupils were not required to analyse the information, to deduce things

from it, to apply it to similar problems or new situations, or to make judgements about its implications. Nor did this low-level demand on thought find itself revealed only in the teacher's task-setting strategies. A look at the list of oral questions which she asked reveals this. The questions are not only predictable in style; they do not demand of pupils more than the simplest of comprehension skills; opportunities for enriching both teaching processes and children's thought forms have been missed; and even the language potential of children talking back to the teacher has been minimised by her readiness to accept one-word answers where these were correct.

What emerges very strongly from this case-studied lesson is, above all, the dependence of the pupils on the teacher. She holds the key not only to all of the data handled but also to every individual step in the process. Independence in learning, with youngsters having some say both in what they learn and how they cope with the task, is more dangerous to, and demanding on, the teacher. But it is at least arguable that these youngsters, at the age of eleven, should be acquiring this facility of independence, the more so in a topic which was soon to culminate in the kinds of learning required on a week's field course in an unfamiliar environment.

Strongest, perhaps, of the teacher's process skills in this extract is her ability to explain. She uses it in providing instructions rather than in exegesis of material to be learned; but it indicates an orderly approach with some potential for application to other learning situations.

This brief review, based upon one main case extract, of the issues in analysing and improving classroom processes and teaching skills for topic work has again concentrated upon raising the problems rather than solving them. Some case studies of how teachers in our sample tackled these problems appear in a later chapter. What follows in this section is a summary of these issues in question format:

Questions about the processes of teaching

Questions of organisation and management

What organisational and management skills do teachers need to tackle topic work effectively?

Questions about teaching mode

How can the three main teaching modes best be employed for topic teaching?

What are the most suitable uses for whole-class work, e.g. for sharing experiences, or knowledge?

What is the function of group work?

How can pupils be assigned to these groups?

Should the criteria for group assignment change from time to time? When? How? Why?

Is individualised learning used? When? How?

Are the pupils really equipped to work independently?

Have they the necessary study skills?

Can they make decisions for themselves?

Are they able to determine in part the directions in which their own work should travel? When they should move on?

Questions about teaching skills

What teaching skills are required of teachers in topic lessons?

How can these skills be refined and improved?

How can lessons be given variety in order to encourage pupils' enthusiasm and curiosity?

How does flexible teaching of the kind implied here affect demands on the general organisation and management skills of the teacher?

Questions about professional development

How, and how often, do you monitor teaching processes in your own classroom?

How can individual teachers become more self-analytical about their practice?

How can they help each other towards this analytical approach?

What is the role and function of in-service training here? How can it operate effectively?

Classroom processes are what teachers delight in calling the 'nitty-gritty' or the 'chalk-face'. As such, they are crucial to the whole business of teaching and learning. But once learning has progressed some way along any given road the teacher is faced with another question: how to monitor that progress. We turn to this main issue in the final section of this chapter.

WHAT HAVE THEY LEARNED?

In the following extracts we come face to face with the fourth main issue in topic work: what have the pupils learned? The first insight can be gained in part of a transcript of a conversation between a caseworker and an eight-year-old pupil who has been following the topic 'Water':

CSW. I've noticed this heading on 'The Water Cycle'. Could you tell me a bit about the water cycle? What does it mean?

Pupil. Well, water cycle means that, when the rain comes down, then the sun comes out, then the rain goes back up and into the clouds. The clouds go across, and they come down, and it keeps going on like that.

CSW. Oh, I see. So, let's be clear about it; you say the rain comes down from the clouds into the earth. Then what happens?

Pupil. The water goes back up.

CSW. How does the water go back up? You said the rain went back up, but you didn't really mean that, did you?

Pupil. Well, they form like puddles and the sun sort of, like sucks them up.

CSW. How does it manage to do that?

Pupil. It shines down and it . . . well, it pulls it up and forms like a cloud.

CSW. There are puddles of water outside this morning. There's one over there out of the window. Can you see that? What will happen to that puddle today? The sun's shining on it: where will it go?

Pupil. Into the air.

CSW. I wonder how it goes up into the air. Strange, isn't it? It's perfectly ordinary water, and we come back this afternoon and it might have disappeared! You've told me it would have gone up into the sky, back into the clouds, is that right? I wonder how we know? How could we get the water out of air? Is there water in the air? I mean, if the water is on its way from that puddle back up into the clouds, then it must be in the air, mustn't it? Do you think so?

Pupil. Well, sort of, certain parts of water go into the air.

CSW. I see. Watch me breathe on the window. What's happened?

Pupil. There's condensation.

CSW. . . . Now what is it that's condensed on the window?

Pupil. Hot air.

CSW. Well it was certainly my hot breath . . . water . . . now it's disappearing . . . where is it going?

Pupil. Into the air.

This extract is fairly and squarely about cognitive learning, both information and concepts. The teacher has 'covered' the water cycle as an element in her topic 'Water'. But what does that coverage mean to an average pupil in the class? In this interview with the pupil the caseworker has tried to explore the youngster's understanding and ability to articulate what she knows. Though teachers hardly have time to use this sort of clinical interview with every pupil on a regular basis, the periodic opportunity to evaluate learning by studying one or two pupils in depth like this is extremely revealing. At this stage, the reader can be left to judge how effective the learning has been; that is, whether the child has grasped the information and the conceptual structure adequately to understand the water cycle in a way appropriate to someone of her age. The question may also need to be considered as to whether any partial learning revealed by the interview is likely to help or hinder more mature understanding later. But clearly, in this topic, there are emergent issues about the value, the nature and the extent of the cognitive learning which has taken place.

Not all learning has to do with cognition, however. Social and attitudinal learning are frequently cited among the intentions for topic work by primary teachers. The next extract looks at the case of a group of relatively deprived ten-year-olds from a slum-clearance area who had just been on a week's cruise on a narrow boat:

CSW. Can you describe for me a typical day on the water?

Pupil. Well, you wake up and you all have your jobs in turn. The people who are cooking breakfast get up a bit earlier, and then you go round asking people what they want. Then you have breakfast. We usually set off on the water after breakfast. When we come to the locks [some of us] get off at the first bridge-halt with our windlasses, run up, undo the locks so that hopefully [the rest] can just drive in without waiting.

CSW. Go on then.

Pupil. At dinner we had sandwiches . . .

CSW. Who made the sandwiches?

Pupil. People in groups, when it's their turn. They have a turn every day. And sometimes we had to stop to empty the loos, a team has to do that . . . and the rubbish disposal . . . and the evening meal. At night we had a walk. Then it was lights out. Before that the teacher on our boat read us a story . . . and we went to sleep.

It shouldn't be imagined, though, that everything which pupils learn from these experiences is positive and comfortable. In a further extract by the same group of youngsters the caseworker is trying to probe what they had learned about everyday life on a canal boat for those who had traditionally made their living on these cramped craft:

CSW. What was it like on that boat?

Pupil. By the door [of the cabin] there was a kind of metal stove. There was a bench on your right-hand side, and a kind of wooden thing and then another bench. At the back there was a little space for the baby to play in, about three metres long and about a metre wide. There was a cupboard for clothes . . . It was very hot in there.

CSW. Did you ask the family what it was like to live on the boat, how they felt about it?

Pupil. I asked her — do you like it on the boat? She says 'I wouldn't be here if I didn't.'

Pupil. . . . She said: 'Shut up and stop asking silly questions.'

Pupils learn cognitively, socially and attitudinally from their experiences in school, including their experiences in topic lessons. They learn both negatively and positively. Teachers need to give some thought to what pupils are learning, how this learning marries with their intentions, and how its progress can be both assessed and recorded. Our case studies revealed that topic work is often not assessed:

CSW. Do you keep written records of children's topic work?

Teacher (of a third-year middle-school class). No.

CSW. How do you assess pupils' work in topic lessons?

Teacher. By the standard of the contents and how much of their own work has gone into it. By the presentation and organisation of the work, e.g. page numbers and contents.

Or again, the form of any permanent assessment other than that of a teacher's impressionistic memory of how the pupil fared in general terms is often limited to one aspect of learning — usually one of content:

CSW. Do you keep written records of children's topic work?
Teaching head (all-through primary). Yes.
CSW. What form do these records take?
Teaching head. Individual charts showing the topics undertaken and the areas of the curriculum covered.

The paucity of record-keeping was often explained as a factor due to the lack of time available to teachers in busy classrooms, but perhaps there was an element, too, of reluctance to admit the need for an activity where the key factor is one of accountability. The teacher of a mixed-age (third- and fourth-year) primary class put it like this:

Teacher. I think in a way [the work] monitors itself in that you can see by looking at the walls and at the display whether or not the standard of work is up to scratch; and by discussing with the children; by their enthusiasm as well. They feed back to you what they are getting out of the topic . . . We do have record sheets, but they're for personal use; and it's in no sense a reflection on us whether or not a child has understood something. These sheets are the only formal record.
CSW. How do you make sure that an individual child in your class is making progress?
Teacher. Well, I suppose it is with discussion yet again.

No one will doubt the value of pupils' work, or their conversation, as means of instant feedback to the teacher about the nature and extent of their learning. But what is lacking in some of the case extracts quoted is any coherent view of the relationship between teacher intentions, classroom processes and evaluation procedures. A parallel omission is an adequate rationale about the kinds of records that need to be kept in a curriculum area which consumes a considerable portion of most pupils' school week. Nor is there any articulation as to whom the information in those records is likely to be useful. So one might proceed to summarise the questions about evaluation and assessment raised by this section of questions that will be explored in detail later in the book.

Given that you have identified your intentions for any given topic and selected appropriate teaching methods, how do you evaluate the pupils' achievements?

Do you evolve methods for tracking the progress they have made

in attitudes to learning?
conceptually?
in learning information?
in acquiring practical skills?
in social learning?
in handling language?
in study skills?
in presenting information?
in making judgements?
in making decisions about their own work and independence?

How is each of the items monitored?

How is each child's progress recorded?

What use do you make of the information yourself?

Do you check over the records when you

review each child's work?
talk to the pupil about his or her work?
plan possible next steps?
plan remedial or stimulation exercises?
consider the next term's syllabus?
write reports for parents or the head?

Do you communicate the information collected to anyone else? To whom? The head teacher? Other staff? The teacher who takes over the class for the next school year? Parents?

How is the information communicated? Do you amend or edit it in any way? How? Why?

Is there some overall system in the school for pooling evaluation and assessment data for planning purposes? How does this system work? Could it be improved?

Above all, do you use your knowledge of pupils' progress in learning to feed back to the pupils themselves, on a regular basis, ideas about how they can improve their own classroom performance, skills and attitudes?

POSTSCRIPT

This list of questions summarises the fourth of the major issues to emerge from our case studies of topic work in progress. The four issues are: the management of topic work at the school level; preparing to teach a topic; classroom processes; and evaluating learning. Together these four issues merge to provide a blueprint for examining a range of effective approaches to topic teaching. In the next five chapters we look at each issue in turn, using case extracts to show how experienced practitioners have tried to answer some of the questions raised in this chapter, augmenting the quotations with some more general discussion where this seems appropriate.

4

Managing the Curriculum

A CASE OF MANAGEMENT IN ACTION

In the previous chapter four major themes or issues in topic work were seen to emerge through our case studies. Here we pursue the first: managing the curriculum. A range of the constituent questions and problems under the broad heading were outlined on pages 68–70. The ways in which these questions arise in practice are neatly illustrated in an extended account from a caseworker's notes, which now follows. This account is a blend of observations and verbatim reports of conversations. It describes the situation of topic work at Dovecote Mill school, whose head teacher is here called Jan.

Dovecote Mill primary school: extracted notes from a case study

The school's setting — first impressions

Take the route A40 out of Nottingham towards the M1 and Derby and in a short while from the city centre you are in well-heeled suburbia. Beyond the last house on the right rise the green wooded slopes of a hill, and Dovecote Mill can be seen. At the summit stands a large secondary comprehensive school; below this school about half-way up the hill against a backdrop of trees is Dovecote Mill primary school. The buildings are modern, glass boxes of varying size, and set at different levels contoured by the shape of the hill on which it was built.

I used the one remaining space in the staff car-park, which contained about half a dozen cars of K and P registration vintage. Looking back down the hill to the road and beyond is the school's catchment area, of owner-occupied, mainly detached houses, suburban, affluent rather than opulent.

I arrived at the school not long after 9.00 am but even before I entered the school visible signs of activity suggested that there had been no general assembly that morning; classes were already engaged on their morning's work.

The route to the head's office lay beyond the entrance 'hall' which was occupied by a class, one of whom responded to my request for directions, politely addressing me as 'sir'.

Interview with the head

Jan is a graduate with PGCE training. She has taught for more than fifteen years and occupied the post of head for eleven years. She is the wife of a colleague and known to me. We are on friendly terms; our relationship is relaxed.

The pupils

There are 327 pupils aged between 5 and 11 years at Dovecote Mill primary school, which was built to accommodate 315. Hence a small library area and the entrance hall are used for teaching. Pupils are differentiated in year groups; each child is effectively randomly assigned to a class which may contain pupils whose range of ability represents that of the population from which they were drawn. (I discovered later however that at least one teacher divides her class into groups according to achievement: within-class streaming.)

My impression of the catchment area was confirmed. Pupils come exclusively from two nearby housing estates consisting almost entirely of detached houses, all privately owned. A graphic illustration of parental status was the fact that, of twenty-one children admitted to the school in April of one year, fourteen were the offspring of lecturers at the local Polytechnic and University, or of school teachers. Parents' evenings are well attended and the mothers of some pupils assist teachers in school hours with, for example, art and craft work.

The growing impression that teaching in this favoured setting must be free from many of the problems and anxieties which beset those of less affluent environments was corrected by the head's account of her perception of the home–pupil–school relationship, and by implication the effect of this relationship on the school's curriculum and the ways in which it is presented.

Jan. An unusual catchment area — brings its own problems.
CSW. What kind of problems does it bring?

Jan. The problems are the expectations of the parents where they expect superhuman teachers. We are not; we are just ordinary teachers, but the expectations from the children are very very great and we have children who don't accept failure easily, who are apprehensive in trying anything new, who are not creative because they are afraid to experiment with paint and clay, in case somebody says 'That's not very good.' Musically very able children, but enthusiastically not very musical because again they haven't got that real enjoyment that comes from making music and making mistakes, and that I think is part of the upbringing of the children.

CSW. So these expectations that the kids are finding it difficult to live up to are very much instrumental: in other words, the kids want to get on and succeed in the system.

Jan. Yes, and therefore they are happier with maths work where there is a progression in which they are confident than trying their hand at creative work where they almost see no limit to it.

The school's curriculum

From the outset our thinking about topic work has been confounded by the problem of definition. What is topic work and what features of it differentiate it from non-topic work in the school's curriculum? Is it synonymous with project work or thematic work? Are topics differentiated from the rest of the curriculum and from each other by reference to their *knowledge content*? As most topics are designated as being *about something*, e.g. windmills, water, pantomime, dinosaurs, living in the 50s, such a differentiating characteristic seems to be part of the common understanding of topic work. I suppose one could have De Bono topics on problem-solving or thinking, topics on inventing hypotheses, but I have not seen accounts of any such topics. It is at least possible that topic work is differentiated from the rest of the curriculum by the nature of the pupils' engagement in it, by *the kind of cognitive or other demands made on pupils.* Possibly *the ways in which teaching and learning are organised*, e.g. the roles of teachers and pupils, the structure of working groups, may give topic work its unique curricular character. To explore the meanings given to topic work is not a sterile exercise in nit-picking semantics, rather it is a case where confusion about terminology is a manifestation of confusion about the intentions, processes and hoped-for outcomes of the form and function of a teaching strategy.

At Dovecote Mill the head sees a fairly clear division between these curricular elements where

(a) there is a set syllabus;
(b) there are (teaching) guidelines;
(c) you can see a progression, a pattern, a development;

and those not possessing these characteristics.

In maths, English, music and PE, which were singled out by Jan for special mention, these criteria are met. There are subjects which may satisfy some but not necessarily all of these criteria, namely art and craft and RE. Thirdly, there are in Jan's words 'the other things' which presumably do not satisfy these criteria, and include environmental studies, health education, 'the bits we would call history and geography, science, and possibly moral education.

These 'other things' obviously include some subjects whose presence in the secondary schools' curriculum is accepted as the staple educational diet of students attending those schools, especially in the early years. As foundations are laid in primary schools for the secondary curriculum it is proper to explore how this is done.

The system currently in use at Dovecote Mill has evolved through 'trial and error', which I take to imply discussions about curriculum content and methods of implementation acted upon and subjected to informal evaluation. The 'other things' are designated topic or interest work. During each year of their life in the school pupils are exposed to six topics, typically, each lasting for half a term. Jan describes her school's attempts to deal with these 'other' elements in the curriculum as '[coping] not very well'. Some of her reservations are concerned with the integration and differentiation of subject knowledge, others with the acquisition of subject-related skills. Her account of the way topics are judged as fit for inclusion suggests that topic work has a built-in entropy which must be countered by the imposition of order. The present policy for topic work is described thus:

All the other things are called topic or interest work and we started off with the idea that within three terms the children could profitably tackle six topics and as long as one was teaching what we identified as geography skills, history skills, then we would accept that within those topics it didn't matter what the subject of the topic was as long as sometimes during the year the children had one that was based on or biased towards geography, one was biased towards history and one biased towards science.

It seems that the ordering principle is based on the definition of skills associated with disciplines or subjects. The knowledge content of a project must, evidently, be such as to function as a vehicle for the acquisition, practice and development of these skills. Clearly, this raises important issues about the nature of these skills. Can general and subject-specific skills be identified? What is the relationship between the manifestation of these skills and knowing the subject matter which provides the context in which these skills function?

An interesting case is that of 'Look — science', which was an important curriculum initiative of Nottinghamshire LEA. A team led by the science adviser responded to surveys conducted locally which suggested that science was under-represented on the primary schools' curriculum, and that the science which was taught left a good deal to be desired, by producing a scheme called 'Look — science'. The scheme consisted of kits of apparatus, teacher's guide and work-cards. At Dovecote Mill the scheme was taken up enthusiastically and science became part of the 'established' curriculum. Jan indicates that science represented in this scheme, at least to her satisfaction, met the criteria listed earlier. This view may not have been shared by her colleagues, who for this or some other (unspecified) reason now prefer to teach science incidentally through topic work. Jan describes these events as follows:

> I am having a little battle at the moment because at one time when we first accepted the 'Look — science' scheme, the Notts scheme, it was great because we were all enthusiastic. We had a science period in the timetable and we did science as science. I could see science, and I could see a progression, some kids doing experiments with air or electricity or water. Now the staff say they prefer the science to go in with the general topic and interest work and I feel we have lost it. I feel now it's become just part of the mishmash of the history and geography and environmental studies even though at any one time in the year one class will do a particular science topic.

The nature of her commitment to 'separate' science is clear from a later comment: 'I was pleased with that because I at least felt that the science had a pattern and a progression, and there was order to *it. Now, at the moment, I feel that there is no order at all.'*

Progression and the means by which progress may be seen to be made is central to Jan's judgement in these curriculum matters. As it is not self-evident how progress in learning science manifests itself I thought it profitable to pursue this line of enquiry as follows:

CSW. How was the progression in science seen?

Jan. It was seen with experiments which they did. A topic was taken like electricity at third-year level and various experiments were worked up to at the level where a child reached his full understanding; we would find it difficult to go any further. And the same with air and water. Some things, like water, lend themselves more easily to the first- and second-year juniors, whereas some things, like electricity, work more with the third and fourth years.

CSW. So the progression could be progression I suppose in two senses. It could be progression that starts off with simple observation, not much thinking but observation, and proceeding through to something like problem-solving.

Jan. In fact this is one of the examples that came out of the fourth year, this system of lights. They started off wiring bulbs to batteries; then they made a Morse code station which goes across the roof, and proceeded to wiring up my room so that I've got three lights on the door. I could see a progression from wiring up one bulb to one battery to working to that over a term. That pleased me; now it's in with everything and I cannot see that progression taking place.

CSW. That could represent three things. It could represent first of all advance in the sense of increased complexity, which might be application, almost a kind of junior technology. It could be an increase in conceptual sophistication. The third thing of course is an advance in the growth of interest in something that's identified like electricity, science or whatever.

Jan. But at the moment it isn't like that, it's very much part of the general topic. Now in some cases if you are doing a creative topic, and we do literature-based topics very often, the science doesn't easily fit into that, so you are either grub-bing round for some tenuous link to bring in the science or you are saying, right, in this case it doesn't work we'll do some separate science on its own. We are falling between the two at the moment.

As things currently stand it would seem that science may occur both as a 'science-based topic' or as a scientific element in a topic, the subject matter of which allows consideration from a number of different perspectives. There seems to be some ambiguity concerning policy here. Staff are encouraged to bias topics towards subjects yielding, in extreme cases, potentially at least, something like a secondary-school curriculum. But it is not clear if staff would be allowed, given a well-argued case, to use exclusively multi-disciplinary topics, i.e. each of which it might be claimed could be regarded from an historical, a geographical, a scientific viewpoint and where languages of words, numbers and space might be used to good effect. Jan refers to 'literature-based topics' where 'the science does not easily fit in . . .'

Topics

During the course of our conversation Jan had referred to particular topics to illustrate points and elucidate policy statements. It seemed likely that some list of categories of topic types might yield a classification which might be useful, if only to probe a little deeper Jan's criteria for accepting them and their application.

In no sense would this be claimed by Jan to be a definitive classification, but it does illuminate the basis of her response to topic proposals. Topics such as 'the study of an author, his works and style of writing' or 'the paintings of David Hockney' are classed as 'creative', presumably because much of the work done by the children involves expressive responses in the form of writing or the production of two- or three-dimensional artefacts. Historical, geographical or scientific studies could not or not easily be undertaken from such starting points. Illustrations of 'non-creative' topics were: windmills, communication, clocks, woodland studies, all of which could form the basis for historical, geographical or scientific studies but which presumably would not preclude opportunities for 'creative' response. Then there are topics almost exclusively undertaken in the summer term which involve visits to sites outside the school of duration from half a day to (e.g.) a week's visit to the Isle of Wight. Also some projects, although few in number, involve the whole school, e.g. 'Folk tales', 'Circles and spheres'. As Jan looked down a list of topics on her desk she described the curriculum offerings as a hotch-potch and implied that she saw their justification in the opportunities they provided to exercise and possibly develop what she called 'reference skills':

The only thing that is keeping me sane at the moment is that I think that no matter what they are doing in that list of topics we are at least doing some reference skills. Because the English work is so well sorted out we are doing a lot of library work, a lot of how to take notes, précis work at the third- and fourth-year level, and that keeps me sane in the topics, not the information that's coming from those topics.

Other instances of topics which reduce Jan's disquiet are those associated with visits, e.g. to the working windmill at North Leverton, to the museum and to Trent Lock in association with 'canals', a week's visit to the Isle of Wight. These 'are worth while', but restricted to summer and have cost implications. One characteristic of topics which either involve visits or are prescribed by them is that they tend towards field work in history or geography, and their use can be justified in terms of their knowledge content and by the use and development of identifiable intellectual processes (= skills?) related to these subjects.

Another instance quoted by Jan of an effective topic was a study of the Bayeux Tapestry, which involved pupils critically examining accounts of the Battle of Hastings from Saxons and Normans. Again an identifiable discipline (history) and some apparently fairly sophisticated intellectual activities associated with historical investigation are involved.

> *CSW. I take it from what you have said that you would judge any proposal for a project in terms of its skill outcomes; in other words you see that this could lead you to imagine them using those skills and if they do that's fine . . . the disquiet you seem to have is in being unable to envisage in any topic the sort of conceptual development that you see in mathematics or any other subjects.*
>
> *Jan. Yes . . . [but the tendency to repetition is worrying, e.g. Dinosaurs are on the list again] I say to the staff: 'The children have done Dinosaurs, they did it in the infants; why are you doing it at second-year level?' The answer always comes back: 'Because we are taking it further at second-year level and there's more to teach, there's more for them to understand.' But I don't really see that; I see the same work. Perhaps the language on the work-sheet is a little bit more difficult, but I really don't see much development.*

Thus, when for example Dinosaurs occur on the topic list Jan is concerned that, when, as might happen, it occurs in different years, there is little evidence of progression. Such a study might feed the imagination or enrich pupils' biological vocabularies but not necessarily contribute significantly to historical conceptual growth.

> *CSW. One wonders what it is about the dinosaurs that is educationally valuable.*
>
> *Jan. It's the fantasy, it's the interest in fantasy; and the length of the words when they are writing them out, the achievement they feel as they learn to spell pterodactyl — but I don't see any value at all. I might see more value in studying dinosaurs if we were doing history as history and dinosaurs were . . . well they fitted into that time when the world was as it was and from whence there was the development of things; we are talking about the history span of time now; I might find it more acceptable then, but we don't do history like that at all.*
>
> *CSW. One of the problems with topic work as you see it is that it tends to be something of a mosaic of disparate little bits that don't necessarily relate, and are not designed to relate to each other.*
>
> *Jan. Yes.*

One might wonder that holding such views Jan allows topic work to occupy the significant place it does on the Dovecote Mill timetable. The answer seems to be in:

> *(a) staff attitudes — they are reluctant to implement the curriculum totally in this (separate subjects) way,*
>
> *(b) the time factor,*
>
> *(c) timetable inflexibility imposed by separate-subject approach,*
>
> *(d) too many separate-subject blocks do not allow for pupils working at different rates.*

In the past a compromise had been worked out which classified topics on disciplinary lines and took account of levels, to ensure that each child received a balanced curriculum appropriate to its stage of development.

> *Jan. At one time one way we tried to get round it was by offering six topics in a year, of which one must be geography, one*

history, one environmental studies. Within, say, geography from the first- to the fourth-year juniors there are the topics which are acceptable to first-year juniors, there are those acceptable to second year and so on. Now that was OK until you had a class teacher who for three years had been doing Australia with the second-year class. They got bored by the topics; the children didn't but the staff did. Similarly, somebody would look at the history topics and say: I am not interested in any of those; I would much rather do the history of pantomime. If that particular teacher is interested in that, won't the children get more out of it than tackling a subject that the teacher doesn't like? So that idea has fallen by the wayside.

CSW. So, the idea of there being not only six topics in each year but also that there is some delineation, stratification and linear development is the result of the staff's response to the scheme?

Jan. Yes, but there are still problems. They found it difficult to bring in the environmental studies then. The people who were very keen on environmental studies felt that the environmental studies were better done at the fourth-year level where the children could get most from the campus and the village and Nottingham, yet it seems an obvious starting point for the first years, when this is the world that they know and this is the campus that they know. So we got into a conflict then between people who had first and fourth years.

Unfortunately this seems to have led to a pattern so repetitive as to cause staff (but not children) to be bored. There were also interesting but apparently unresolved conflicts on the relationship between topic and level; e.g. does one teach environmental studies in Year I 'because its an obvious place to start' or leave it to Year IV when it can be made respectably scientific and pupils will 'get more out of the campus and the village'? I tried to summarise Jan's scepticism in the course of our conversation as follows:

CSW. Your doubts about topic work are really about curriculum organisation. The question is: at what point is it appropriate to induct kids in a fairly systematic way into the beginnings of what we regard as the discipline of knowledge? Is that OK?

Jan. That's right, yes.

CSW. There are various ways of trying to cope with it. One is to give them a fairly orthodox quasi-secondary timetable of disciplines; the other is to use other ways which have got branded topic work or project work for various reasons. The reasons seem to be something to do with self-contained half-term stints, tasks or series of related tasks around some common theme.

Jan. That's right; but in fact the tasks are very often exactly the same regardless of what the topic is. Again it's covering the writing skills more than anything, which is really all the topic is becoming.

Maths, English (and Science?) across the curriculum

The proposal to abandon 'Look — science' as a discrete curriculum element and integrate it with topic work implies a willingness on the part of the teachers to take advantage of the opportunities which a topic offers to introduce scientific knowledge related to that topic and involve them in scientific ways of getting that knowledge. Similarly it would be reasonable to expect various forms and functions of the languages of words and number to be explored in the variety of contexts offered by topics.

In practice this is not clearly visible except possibly in the case of English. Jan's view is that topics tend to regress to little more than exercises involving comprehension and writing skills, as the previous quotation suggests. Maths is a very interesting case.

CSW. How do numerical skills fit into some of these topics?

Jan. Really not very much at all — that list that you've got this year, as you see it's only going to come into machines. In fact the maths tends to go through very much on its own in the school. We've got a very strong mathematical person in charge. We were fortunate in that, being only a 5 to 8 school and then developing slowly into a 5 to 11, we had a lot of time to sort out that scheme, both practically and on the computation side, and therefore maths very much stands alone in what we do.

To counter this isolation of mathematics the topic 'Circles and spheres' is shortly to be undertaken. It will involve the whole school, in both mathematical and art and craft work. Whole-school projects also serve another important function, that of providing Jan with a demonstration that, for reasons which are not entirely clear, pupils evidently progress, grow in knowledge and skills, level and repertoire as they move through the school.

Jan. The whole school is going to be involved in this 'circles and spheres' topic which is leading up to an art and craft evening. We like whole-school projects of this kind because the teachers actually see the development of children's skills, when you've got the whole range from infant to fourth year.

CSW. Do you mean the skills that have been developed in other contexts are being applied at different levels?

Jan. That's right. For example, colouring, painting, paper sculptures. You suddenly realise that progress is being made with skills, but how it is coming out of the mess that we have got — I don't know.

CSW. It sounds like using the project as a massive test which reassures teachers that progress is being made.

Jan. Yes, yes.

It would appear that the reasons for the apparently small and patchy occurrence of mathematics across the topic curriculum are complex, but three strands emerge as components of a possible explanation.

(a) A carefully constructed mathematics scheme involving practical as well as theoretical work results in levels of achievement which satisfy staff (and parental?) expectations.

(b) Many topics do not lend themselves to mathematical treatment.

(c) Whereas in the case of English the staff feel competent to design tasks and work-cards at a level perceived to be appropriate to each child's level of competence, this is not the case with mathematics.

It follows that Jan's view of the relationship between topic and a discipline, say, mathematics, is that of learning the topic through mathematics rather than learning mathematics through the topic. The application of mathematics learnt in maths classes takes precedence over finding topic-related problems, the solution of which may be sought in mathematical models or the design and use of which requires *new* mathematical learning. (Two lessons which were later observed contained examples of such problems.)

CSW. Looking at your list of topics, there seem in some cases to be clear relationships between numerical skills or mathematical skills; seasons, clocks, water.

Jan. It would come in but not in the same way as they are using their reading skills.

CSW. Why do you think that is? I've heard this before and I must admit I find it quite intriguing that when people talk, as since Bullock they have talked, about language across the curriculum, not many teachers find this at all threatening or puzzling. They say, we do use the English language not only to report on what we've seen, done, thought, we also think in words. But for every argument that's deployed in that direction I suppose the same thing would apply to the use of numbers. Yet, oddly enough, number across the curriculum, in your case number across topics, seems not to happen to the same degree.

Jan. I think that there is perhaps more of a problem. When a class teacher is taking a topic lesson it very often starts with some kind of taught part of the lesson, giving information, or directing children towards information. The work that the children do is usually work-cards, comprehension work, drawing. Where you've got mixed ability in the class they can be directed to tasks matched to their abilities. Now if it was something that was going to follow mathematically, the mathematical range in the class is so great that I just wonder if it would be as easy to achieve this match with follow-up work on the card.

CSW. If that were true, and I have no reason to doubt it — I suppose what it means at the end of the day is that for the younger end of your classes their competence in mathematical language is simply inadequate. It might imply for your older kids, the 9s probably, 10s certainly, that there could be, potentially, a mathematical component which might be under-exploited!

Jan. Actually that's interesting, because, having followed up a talk with the maths person only this week, that is why we are now setting off on this practical maths topic for the whole school. [Circles and spheres]

The 'natural history' of a topic

Origins. Of the twelve assistant teachers at Dovecote Mill, eleven are in sole charge of a class for a year. Music, PE, any 'hall period' and games are timetabled and taught by specialist teachers; the remainder of the curriculum is organised temporally and 'spatially' (i.e. in groupings) by the class teachers. These teachers enjoy freedom to divide their class into groups and, as in the three classes investigated to date, simultaneously teach English, mathematics and topic (or interest) work.

Prior to the current school term each teacher provides the head with a 'forecast' of the work to be covered during the term, in mathematics, English, science (?) and topic work. The latter is, typically, a statement of intent to cover two named topics. As far as possible Jan wishes to provide, in topic work, a balanced curricular diet of history-biased, geography-biased and science-biased topics, and to avoid repetition of topics covered by pupils in previous years. Other than this, evidence of commitment of a member of staff and that an adequate range of resources is available is sufficient to allow the topic to proceed. Jan rarely, if ever, has rejected a topic but regards it as her responsibility to advise and amend. She may ask for more information, for example, a 'flow chart' mapping progress through the topic.

There is a good deal of staffroom chat about the feasibility and resourcing of topics. Occasionally two classes might work together. Given that the teachers of these classes have different interests, knowledge or expertise, that both regard the topic as a suitable vehicle and the two teachers involved are personally and professionally compatible, then collaboration is possible. Such arrangements are not frequent, presumably because of the comprehensive integration of the two classes' methods of working which would be required. Another variant is when two parallel classes undertake different topics, pupils being allowed to choose. This arrangement is subject to the same constraints as in the previous case. Occasionally a topic may last the whole term.

Thus, class teachers determine the topics to be taught, they map out for their forecast content, to some degree the 'skills' involved, and show that resources required to service the topic exist and can be obtained. Jan's professional judgement is based on evidence of commitment and the availability (and cost?) of resources. She prefers to consult, advise and amend rather than reject a topic forecast, and may engineer links with curriculum subjects, e.g. to bring music of the 50s into the music 'syllabus' of the class doing the topic 'Living in the 50s'.

Now the class teacher, given the go-ahead, incorporates the topic into the flexible arrangements of class teaching. At least four hours per week will be spent on topic work, the pupils being engaged on a range of tasks frequently guided by work-sheets, typically in groups of about five and six pupils.

Occasionally a topic proves abortive. The reasons given in the two examples quoted were failure of resource and boredom. The first depended on paintings which did not arrive at the school when required. The second, on oil exploration, failed to hold the attention of pupils, possibly because it was conceptually beyond the group of eight-year-olds or for some other unknown reason. Sex bias in some topics was quoted as a reason for their failure with 'half' the class: 'the girls sat through bridges and machines'.

Later the teachers' topic forecasts will be examined. From Jan's account the impression given is of variation in the amount of detail given and possibly variation in the kind of information given by teachers. Are clear statements of intentions, anticipated outcomes of learning, given? In what terms are teaching/learning processes described? Is there agreement about what counts as evidence that pupils have learnt what they are expected to learn?

Does topic work provide a suitable basis for later work at the secondary school 'up the hill'? What are the secondary teachers' expectations, and are these reaslised?

CSW. This transition between your school and the comprehensive school, how much collaboration is there? What is the relationship between the comprehensive school and your school? Obviously, teachers at that school have got some expectations; and in the case of subjects like mathematics the expectations may be clear enough in terms of expected competences at that level, but for the rest of the curriculum like history, geography and so on, what is the relationship?

Jan. There is no contact at all and in fact we don't talk about it; we don't seem to have much communication. The only feedback is from the children who have gone and they refer to note-taking, looking for the main ideas, using an index, as useful skills acquired during primary schooling. That's back to what keeps me sane thinking about the topic at the moment.

CSW. I may share your concern of what seems to be the lack of conceptual development in topic work, but presumably it could be argued that if pupils were acquiring these 'thinking' skills and are showing coping strategies when they come to more formal operations one wonders if we ought really to be too concerned about the absence of well-structured conceptual maps in their minds. But it obviously still does concern you.

Jan. It concerns me very much, just looking, as I say, haphazard . . . and the only time when I really settle down happily is when I feel the whole school is working on a topic like the literature-based topic; and we have children writing the books, a newspaper being presented in the school, reporters rushing round interviewing people, mums coming in typing the books *the children have written; and there I see some output of it. Otherwise I tend to see scrappy folders with odd sheets, with 'fill in the missing words, answer these questions'.*

Record-keeping

Record-keeping in the sense of a record of tasks completed and of achievement, which is accepted as a professional responsibility in maths, writing and phonic skills, does not occur in topic work.

> *CSW. Record-keeping in the senses of both keeping a record of what is being done and recording the achievement of pupils in that task: what form do such records take in topic and non-topic work?*
>
> *Jan. We don't do anything on that for topic work. We do it for maths, phonic skills, handwriting and creative writing; but keeping a record of the children's work for topic — absolutely nothing. What is more worrying, nothing for science. We are back to this business of science in with everything else. I can't see the development there. We are neither isolating the skills you need for science nor recording children's achievement of them.*

Some questions raised by the Dovecote Mill case

There is no such thing as a 'typical' case, if by that one implies that most schools will exhibit most features of the case and that generalisations can be drawn from the specific instances observed and described. Nevertheless, over a number of cases, particular responses to problems did recur and approaches to solving these problems were often common across a range of quite different schools. Dovecote Mill can be said to be quite usual in the difficulties it encounters in tackling some of the questions under the broad theme of curriculum management. If we examine the sub-issues and questions outlined under this theme in Chapter 3 we shall see some dimensions of this recurrent approach. The paragraphs that follow examine these questions in so far as we can deduce the responses from the quoted case-study extract above.

Questions of policy

Has the school an agreed policy for topic teaching?

Is it clearly laid down?

Is it accessible to, and known by, all staff?

By what mechanism does the head ensure that staff abide by its principles?

What kinds of consultation went into its formulation?

The answer to the first question appears to be largely in the negative. The case-study extract clearly implies that the school has three methods for arriving at curriculum decisions.

First, there is some democratic consultation between head and staff. This is exemplified in the school transition from 'science' teaching to teaching science as and when it fits into a topic or theme. Jan, as head, was unhappy both at the prospect of this change and at the result (very little science is now taught and pupils' progress in scientific knowledge or skills is hard to track). But the democratic decision of the staff won the day.

Secondly, there is informal staffroom discussion, which apparently is concerned mostly with the 'feasibility and resourcing' of topics. Little joint effort by teachers results from this chat.

Thirdly, one deduces that individual teachers decide upon their own topic titles and devise their own content. The teacher is the strongest single influence, then, upon the curriculum — though subject to some control from the head.

This head-teacher control is exercised through the mechanism by which teachers make 'forecasts' of the topic titles, along with an outline of topic content, to be covered each term. These statements of intent do not appear to be very detailed; in fact, they represent the minimal check that school policy is being adhered to.

School policy itself has to do partly with organisation and partly with curriculum balance. It is laid down that six topics, each of half a term's duration, shall be covered each year; and that two shall have a historical bias, two a geographical one and two a scientific emphasis. This discovery in effect disposes also of the following questions on the theme set out in chapter 3:

Question of curriculum balance and monitoring

Who ensures that a child's curriculum is balanced across each school year?

Across a school career?

How is this achieved?

Who monitors that the work is covered by the teachers?

How does the monitoring take place?

This brings us, then, to the set of questions which seek to examine the management structure of the school and the roles that individuals play within it:

Questions of school management structure

Which staff have special responsibility for implementing topic-work policy?

What are their respective roles? Responsibilities? Powers?

When do they meet?

Who chairs the meetings?

What form do the meetings take?

We have seen that, at one level, Jan monitors the *outlines* of what the teachers plan. There is evidence in the extract, however, of underlying tensions. 'I am having a little battle at the moment,' she says. She has lost ground over the policy for teaching separate science; and she 'says to the staff: "The children have done Dinosaurs, they did it in the infants; why are you doing it at second-year level?" The answer always comes back: "Because we are taking it further . . ." But I don't really see that. I see the same work.' Overall, the control of the curriculum, decision-making, and the implementation of policy appear to have been neglected, the potential middle-management personnel ignored and the real curriculum power of the individual teacher given mechanisms for bypassing the spirit of school-level decisions. Perhaps as a result of this situation, issues about curriculum content are not clearly resolved, as a look at the following questions reveals:

Questions of intention, content, skills and integration

Are there clear sets of aims and intentions for topic work?

Are there clear guidelines about the practical and social skills pupils need to acquire?

Are there sets of concepts identified as necessary for learning?

Is a certain content regarded as essential?

Are staff aware of these agreed skills, concepts and data?

Are topic titles selected at school level? How? By whom? On what criteria?

How are decisions made about the duration of topics?

What criteria are used for deciding which work is integrated?

How does topic work relate to work done in basic subjects?

In other areas of the curriculum?

Once more, the answer to the first question is apparently negative: the caseworker did not discover any formal list of aims and intentions. He did discover a kind of tentative typology of topics into 'creative' and 'non-creative', 'visits' and 'those involving the whole school'. These types may have implications for deducing intention. Thus creative topics are, presumably, designed to give opportunities for the expressive arts, the non-creative ones are probably data-based, visits may be related to developing observation skills and the whole school themes to raising pupils' awareness of some specific idea or concept. But the links between typology and intention may be somewhat tenuous. No systematic attempt to set out skills and concepts appropriate for acquisition and development through topic work in the primary years appears to have been attempted in such a way that it has become a shared professional goal for all staff in the school.

As far as content is concerned, some clues to Jan's own thinking are available in the extract: she sees topics as a way of covering ground which might formerly have existed in inconvenient subject-specific timetable blocks. Integration threatens to unbalance this subject-specific learning — one teacher may give *every* topic a literary bias, for example; and we have seen how basic mechanisms for coping with this danger have evolved.

The distinctions between 'subjects' and topics are drawn out by the caseworker. Subjects have a set syllabus, predictable teaching methods and a clear progression or sequence of development. Topics do not. Integrating 'subjects' and making links between topic work and other curriculum areas are a process which causes some difficulties. Pupils' mathematical ability, reportedly, is too disparate to allow this; criteria for integration in maths and science at least are unclear; only 'reference skills', the higher reading skills, are central to and practised within the topic-work context with any facility.

As far as any essential content to topic work is concerned, it is clear that staff autonomy precludes any view of a 'core curriculum' essential to the primary child. With 'no contact' and 'no communication' between primary and secondary school the total irrelevance of any such core to the pupils' future education is assured. It is this lack of clear directional aims that perhaps makes Jan unsure of the answers to questions of progression in learning such as those outlined in chapter 3.

Questions of progression

How do staff monitor what the children have learned?

How do they record the progress that pupils have made?

Are these monitoring and recording strategies sufficiently flexible to cope with all facets of the pupil's learning?

Perhaps all that is necessary here is to call to mind Jan's statement: 'We don't do anything on that for topic work. We do it for maths, phonic skills, handwriting and creative writing; but keeping a record of the children's work for topic — absolutely nothing'.

So we come to the last set of questions about curriculum management, those concerned with teacher self-evaluation and their in-service professional development.

Questions of professional development and accountability

How do teachers keep up to date with thinking in this field?

Do they attend courses?

How are staff selected for courses?

Is the professional development of each individual teacher monitored? By whom? How?

Do teachers evaluate their own work? How?

Is there a clear rationale about what constitutes successful topic work?

Is this applied regularly to work in progress? When? By whom?

Who is responsible for amendments of policy, or improvements in practice?

Does the school communicate its topic-work policies to parents? To other interested parties: advisers, any feeder schools, the comprehensive school? When? How?

Does it foster co-operation with other interested outsiders: in industry, in the public services, from parents?

This set of questions has two perspectives: how the teachers view their own work, and how they make use of and communicate with the world beyond the classroom door. In fact, little evidence has emerged from the present case extract to answer these questions. There is almost no evidence at all about how in-service training and professional development are handled; and one must not draw any kind of unwarranted conclusions from silence. We have gleaned that no contact takes place with the comprehensive school; that the head has some knowledge of what the pupils do in the infant school; and that the advisory service has not apparently intervened or assisted in the school's struggle to find a rationale for topic work. As for links with the community, there is mention of visits outside school but not of visitors to the school. It is clear from the early paragraphs of the extract that parents are of a particular social stratum, and that they provide a source of informal pressure upon the curriculum and teaching method. These professional parents are clearly a rich potential resource: their presence in classes would certainly open pupils' eyes to interesting facets of the outside world. We have no evidence of whether or how this resource is exploited.

Thus we have completed our review of Dovecote Mill's approach to curriculum management. The results are certainly mirrored in other cases in this study. Dovecote Mill represents one group of case-study schools: those which are struggling with questions and seeking solutions. Some other schools would claim to have reached some conclusions about handling the topic-work curriculum; and in the remainder of this chapter it is these conclusions which are reviewed. In a sense, then, this chapter moves from a school which has described a set of *practical procedures* to examples of schools where, in part at least, there is an *articulated rationale* for managing the topic-work curriculum. We shall examine this rationale under the same six headings as form the groups of questions above and in chapter 3.

(i) Questions of policy

Just as Dovecote Mill exemplified one state of play in schools' approaches to topic work, so Starvale, a school in a more typically mixed social setting, exemplifies another: that of the articulated rationale. Typically, such a rationale finds expression in a staff handbook. We can begin our examination of Starvale's policy for topic work with a quotation from just such a handbook. It should be noted that at Starvale the term 'topic work' is replaced by the description 'integrated studies'.

Starvale staff handbook, Extract A: exhibit from a case study

Integrated Studies is a term used to describe primary-school work in which subject disciplines can be brought together in the study of particular areas of interest.

Integrated studies is not a subject in itself but rather an approach to learning which draws upon the traditional subject disciplines.

It is an approach which offers to the school the opportunity to harness what the Plowden Report called 'the intense interest shown by young children in the world about them', and to use it to motivate children's learning. Learning becomes meaningful and enjoyable to the children.

As long ago as the 1931 Report it was stated that 'The curriculum is to be thought of in terms of activity and experience rather than of knowledge to be acquired and facts to be stored.' Integrated Studies provides precisely such opportunities for practical first-hand experience which makes learning relevant and effective.

However, such learning has tended to be unorganised in the past. The recent Primary Survey suggests that 'schools should have a clear overall plan for work of this kind, so that the ideas and skills as well as information suitable to the children are extended and developed as the children move through the school'.

These guidelines are intended to provide a 'clear overall plan' for integrated studies at this school, bearing in mind the particular needs of our children. Experience and advice have been drawn upon in their preparation.

The guidelines are not for one reading, they are for reference again and again to assist the teacher in planning work. They do not constitute a 'final' scheme, nor, it is hoped, will they ever do. The needs of the school will change, the curriculum will develop and these things should be reflected in these guidelines. The guidelines are contained within a loose-leaf folder so that more appendices can be added to give further practical advice.

Our receiving secondary school welcomes this approach and it dovetails extremely well with their own approach to Humanities.

Finally, it is very important to mention that in the primary school the effectiveness of the children's learning depends more than anything else upon the quality of the teacher/child relationship and upon the enthusiasm of committed teachers. Though these guidelines are intended to put structure and planning into our teaching, it is in no way intended that this should be at the expense of all spontaneity and interest.

If used carefully, these guidelines will assist the teacher to maintain and develop the quality of the children's learning whilst at the same time preserving flexibility and spontaneity.

THE APPROACH

This approach to primary-school work is referred to in many ways. It is frequently called 'project work', 'topic work' or 'environmental studies'.

The approach is not new. For many years children have studied 'topics' in which subject boundaries are blurred or broken down. It has often been said that the primary-school child is not concerned with history or geography or science but is just interested in a myriad of things. We should grasp this interest, this curiosity, and use it to motivate meaningful learning. Children learn best when they are interested, and the learning of reading, measurement, mapwork or anything else will be most effective when the child can understand the relevance of what he is doing, when it is useful to his curiosity, when he wants to know.

It is important that most of the work which children do should be concerned with their local environment. This is particularly relevant at our school.

Firstly because we need to pay particular attention to the basic skills of language and number and, as the Primary Survey pointed out, this will not be done by falling back to a narrow, formal curriculum, but will best be achieved by maintaining and developing a broadly based curriculum to provide the children with an enriched experience. Our children need to examine and be stimulated by the people and places and 'things' in their own environment, then they will be more able and more willing to respond in terms of language development. We should find things in the child's own environment which will stimulate a response from the child.

Secondly, it is important that the child should study his own environment in order to understand it and come to an appreciation of his place within it.

Not all of the work will be locally based. There may well be a topic which is far removed . . . Red Indians for example, Space Travel and many others. These can be just as valid if they motivate meaningful learning. Geography will be discussed later and we shall see that the study of distant lands is very relevant in the primary school. However, the primary-school child's experience is very local in terms of both space and time. It is from this experience that we should base our work in the development of the child.

It follows from what has been said that since the majority of the work will be locally based it can and should be very practical, offering the child the opportunity to go and see 'things', to 'do' things. He should gain firsthand experience as much as possible. Such work will provide a multitude of opportunities to develop language, maths and many other skills.

We should grasp every opportunity to take children outside the school for firsthand experience, whether this be close to school or much further away. (See Appendix 1 for school journey guidelines.) We should as often as possible bring worthwhile visitors into school to meet, talk to and work with the children. We should also make the best possible use of radio and TV, not slavishly following a multitude of programmes but using the media as resources which form part of planned work.

We should, of course, be constantly seeking to develop skills and attitudes in the primary school, but this has often been done in a rather haphazard way through topic work. Hence there have sometimes been gaps in the child's skills and on occasion skills have been repeated far too often. These guidelines seek to help the teacher to plan topics in a structured, meaningful yet flexible way so that skills are acquired and practised progressively. It should lead to continuity of learning throughout the school. The major implication of a progressive yet flexible system of integrated studies is that skills acquired, attitudes dealt with and content covered should be recorded and the child's progress evaluated. It is hoped that the recording system within these guidelines will fulfil this implication.

The practical details of planning, recording and evaluating will be deal with in the following sections of the guidelines.

The approach to integrated studies will vary slightly throughout the school. Much of the work in the nursery and lower infants is concerned with the development of early language skills. The development of these skills is dealt with in detail in the language scheme but it is important to note here that suitable integrated studies work can provide superb opportunities to stimulate language development. We have already seen that the child's environment should provide much upon which to base responses from the child. We at this school are very concerned with language development; the children require much stimulus. Integrated studies is the perfect vehicle for such work.

Later in the school we should be concerned with the development of higher skills and attitudes. For example we should, through topic work, seek to develop objectivity, critical thinking and the ability to hypothesise.

Since we wish to give the children firsthand experience, the opportunity to carry out much practical work, to solve problems, etc., our teaching methods must be appropriate. There will, of course, be times when the class must be taught together — 'chalk and talk', there will be times when group work will be appropriate and other times when the children will work individually, but the accent should be upon group and individual work in an informal atmosphere.

SUMMARY

1. This approach to learning can be highly motivational.
2. Most of the work should be based in the local environment because:
   (a) The needs of our children demand enriched experiences to which they can respond in language. The local environment can provide unlimited opportunities to stimulate such responses.
   (b) The children need to understand their environment.
   (c) Firsthand experience is most important.
3. This approach ensures continuity and progression.
4. The approach will vary according to the children's stage of development, but the planning will be the same.
5. Teaching methods must be flexible.

THE ROLE OF THE SUBJECT DISCIPLINES

A topic can include almost any of the subject disciplines when they are appropriate . . . However, the teacher must ensure that over the school year curriculum balance is achieved and that the child has worked in all areas of the curriculum in approximately the same proportion. Some subject disciplines may at times be taught *separately from the topic, but an overall balance should be achieved through the school year.*

Here at Starvale, then, staff consultation and the expertise of outside agencies have been used to produce a policy document for use by existing and future staff and to counter criticism from an HMI Report on primary education. Mechanisms by which the head ensures that staff abide by its principle are built into the scheme; but these are best discussed in section (vi) below.

(ii) Questions of curriculum balance and monitoring

What is a balanced curriculum? In practical terms it is usually defined by the teachers in terms of subject representation within the topic. For example, ground covered by a topic on water might include poems about the sea, the mathematics of volume and weight, some water conservation and pollution issues, the sources of water, the water cycle, how to paint water, the use of water power in the past and present, and musical attempts to reproduce the sound of water. This would be considered a 'balanced' topic. A topic on water that concentrated solely on one or two of these facets would be 'unbalanced', i.e. it would lack a truly cross-disciplinary approach. So the question of balance is one of subject representation within the topic and of attitudes towards this problem. The Starvale handbook has a detailed rationale of the issue. For example, of history it says:

Starvale staff handbook, Extract B

HISTORY
'The traditional junior school syllabus was a four-year gallop through the centuries culminating in modern times in the fourth year. The whole thing was then repeated in the secondary school. This attempt at chronological coverage and an accumulation of knowledge shows not only a lack of understanding of children's development, it also invites criticism as an unsatisfactory way to study history. Most primary schools have rightly abandoned the strictly chronological approach, preferring instead an integrated approach to topics as the study of history in particular patches . . . It is tempting for teachers — particularly if they are historians — to be eloquent about, for example, medieval kings and wars, but greater service will be done to children by giving them experiences

which help them to understand what the life of the people was really like. This is best done at first hand . . .' K. Thorne (Former County History Adviser)

The above quotation summarises well what the primary-school approach to history teaching should be. We should not be concerned with teaching the children a body of historical facts arranged in chronological order. We should be concerned with teaching the children about the ways in which historians look at things. Through history, topics are examined from a particular viewpoint and certain kinds of questions are asked, about change and its causes. We should be 'leading the children towards an understanding of historical change and the causal factors involved' (Primary Survey). This task will involve developing in the children an awareness of time and sequence, the ability to work with, and later evaluate, historical evidence, and the ability to empathise.

It will be seen in Section 2 that the concept of 'cause and consequence' is used as part of the basis for our topic planning and that the historical skills mentioned above are listed in developmental stages to be planned into topics.

The implication is that our history teaching should deal with places the children know and can visit to 'see' history. It should concern evidence which they can use and handle (grandma's mementoes, local buildings) in order to help them empathise and learn what it was like.

This is not to say that pure history should be scrubbed from the timetable. Far from it. Children are greatly interested in people and an important part of their development is the exploration of human behaviour. For this reason it is essential to give the children a good diet of stories about real historical events, e.g. Battle of Hastings, Gunpowder Plot, and also legends, myths and stories of King Arthur, Robin Hood, etc., since such stories are an important part of the nation's culture and way of life.

And of subject disciplines overall, and their place in a topic-work scheme, the handbook concludes:

Starvale staff handbook, Extract C

1. Any appropriate subject discipline can contribute to a topic.
2. Subject disciplines should also be taught separately when appropriate.
3. The teacher must ensure curriculum balance over an

academic year. (See Section 4.1.)

4. *The emphasis in our history teaching should be upon helping the children understand 'change' and 'cause' and 'what it was really like'.*

5. *The emphasis in our geography teaching should be upon helping the children to understand the man/environment relationship through a continuous study of the local environment, distant places, maps and weather.*

6. *The emphasis in our science teaching should be upon the development of scientific skills and understanding rather than upon scientific facts only.*

7. *Language and maths work in integrated studies is intended to complement these respective schemes and provide opportunities to practise and enhance skills meaningfully.*

(iii) Questions of school management structures

Starvale's handbook gives little guidance on this, though some deductions can be made. Clearly, the leadership for this initiative in topic teaching has emanated from the head. As we shall see in section (vi) below, it is to him that teachers are responsible and accountable. In Starvale's case, little use is made, apparently, of other possible agencies or middle management: the deputy, year-group leaders or holder of responsibility posts.

(iv) Questions of intention, content, skills and integration

The broad intentions for topic work at Starvale have been illustrated in the extract under section (i) above. We shall return in more detail to this question again in section (v), when we consider how these broad aims are turned into specific objectives for a piece of topic work and what the objectives are. Meanwhile, the major focus of attention will be on questions of *what* children learn: the concepts, skills and data. The Starvale handbook sets out its position unequivocally:

Starvale staff handbook, Extract D

Good topic planning is essential to the achievement of [our] aims, but before planning can take place it is necessary to understand the process involved. This process involves five main components:

116

1. *CONTENT*

2. *CONCEPTS*

3. *KEY IDEAS*

4. *SKILLS*

5. *GENERAL, SOCIAL, PHYSICAL SKILLS AND ATTITUDES*

CONTENT

The topic or project title, whatever it may be, will provide the content which the children will study. Through this study the children will develop concepts, general skills, social skills, physical skills and attitudes. They will also come to understand certain key ideas and progressively develop important subject skills.

The content may be 'Shops', 'Houses' or indeed any title which the teacher considers to be relevant, meaningful and a suitable vehicle for skill development.

We have already seen that children learn best when they are well motivated, and carefully chosen topics can indeed inspire excellent learning in the children. Furthermore we have also seen that our children need to study the local environment and be provided with many opportunities for firsthand experience in order to stimulate language development. These factors should all be borne in mind by the teacher when selecting a suitable topic.

Two other factors should also be considered. Firstly the 'interest age' of the children concerned so that topics are suitable for age groups, and secondly our own interests as teachers. We are not all interested equally in all possible topics. Some topics would inspire us more than others. Since our enthusiasm affects that of the children we should play to our strengths and interests where possible.

One further consideration when choosing content is that of repetition. These guidelines are intended to ensure that skills are not repeated but extended and the same should apply to content. Children will become bored if they 'do' the same thing again. Since the environment offers us an unlimited range of possible topics there would seem to be little reason for the child to repeat what has been done before. We should confine our topics to titles which are limiting enough to avoid the need for repetition. For example, 'Water' would be too broad a topic title but 'Floating and Sinking' or 'Pond Life' would not. If repetition is unavoidable then we must ensure that

(a) *Content taught in lower infants should not be repeated before middle junior, and upper infants/upper junior.*

(b) *Where such repetition must take place the content is at a higher and more appropriate level. (Planning forms should be kept to assist.)*

In the case of Mapping and Weather . . . the repetition will take place throughout school life but should progress according to the stages listed.

Our individual children's record sheets will inform receiving teachers of content covered so that the teacher can plan accordingly.

It is important that we should each be free to choose topic content. An imposed list would inhibit the teacher's enthusiasm and thus that of the children. In the primary school, integrated studies should be a vital and exciting part of the curriculum. Content limitations could have the effect of making the work repetitive for the teacher and boring for the children. Where possible this freedom to choose content should be used wisely in the avoidance of content repetition.

CONCEPTS

A concept is a general idea which represents a group of things, actions or relationships, having certain characteristics in common (e.g. fruit, mountain, market).

Some concepts are quite simple whilst others are more complex. It is important that we teach concepts for several reasons. Firstly because to attempt the teaching of facts only would be futile. Facts are so numerous that to teach them all would be impossible, the number of facts increases daily and can soon become out of date. Secondly, children develop a growing store of concepts which help them to understand and interpret new situations and experiences as they arise. Thirdly, concepts act as organisers and summaries for us when meeting new experiences and finally they are anchor points in learning to which the teacher will want to return from time to time in order to stress their role in learning.

In integrated studies three concepts have been identified which are common to history, geography, science and most of the primary-school curriculum. They are:

Similarity/Difference

Continuity/Change

Cause/Consequence

These three concepts are concerned with ways of classifying and examining subject matter.

Similarity/Difference is obviously concerned with classifying. Continuity/Change can be used to examine Then and Now or even Then and Then through the study of the same place at different times. Cause and consequence arise through the need to consider why some things differ from others and why things change.

It is not expected that the children will be able to grasp those concepts although it may be possible in some cases that children will become able to use and begin to understand the actual terms.

The main use of these three concepts is for teachers in planning topics. Their use will enable teachers to examine possible content in a selective way so that the content can be 'pruned' to that which is relevant and meaningful and contains a relatively coherent progression in concept development.

It has been a common practice in topic planning to draw up a topic 'web' . . .

This [kind of] topic web concerns itself only with those things related to [e.g.] 'Canals', and all of the content in it is related to that topic. It would be possible to develop the web much further including many more items which, it could be argued, would be related to the topic of 'Canals'. Yet it would be difficult to show a purposeful relationship between [e.g.] 'bridge construction' and 'water birds' or 'holidays'.

Alternatively, the three concepts can be used as 'organisers' around which the content can be grouped. This has the effect of pruning and limiting the content to those items which are relevant and purposeful. Furthermore, when the concepts have been used in the planning of content it should be certain that what is taught is conceptually based and that those concepts will be continuously developed.

The content for 'Canals' organised in this way may look like this:

SIMILARITY/ DIFFERENCE	CAUSE/ CONSEQUENCE	CONTINUITY/ CHANGE
Canal home/ land home	Poor roads/canal development	Canals past and present
Canal art	Coming of	Boat types
Canal flora/ alternative habitat	railways/decline of canals	
	Canal buildings	
	Locks, aqueducts, tunnels, bridges	
	Building problems	

KEY IDEAS

It is important that the teacher is clear about exactly what he wishes the child to understand from the topic. We are concerned that the children should be developing their conceptual awareness and that they should acquire and develop skills. We should also be clear about what we wish them to understand from the content. We should not be seeking simply the acquisition of facts but an understanding of some key ideas which should come about through studying the content.

For example, a study of 'Canals' might have the following as key ideas:

1. To help the child understand the idea that canal people had a culture of their own which was different from the culture of 'land' people.

2. To help the child understand the idea that the function of canals has changed.

3. To help the child understand the idea that the coming of the railways was a cause of the decline of the canals.

It can be seen that these key ideas can be closely allied to the three concepts.

Approached in this way we define the knowledge component of the topic, precisely and meaningfully.

SKILLS

The acquisition of skills is a vital part of the child's learning. We must ensure that

120

(a) We know and can plan exactly which skills we wish to teach and develop through a particular topic.

(b) Skills are practised and developed in a progressive and continuous way. Children should neither repeat skills already acquired too often, nor be asked to practise skills which they are not ready to attempt.

The use of these guidelines should ensure that the above conditions are attained.

The skills appropriate to Integrated Studies have been listed under these headings.

Language Skills
Mathematical Skills
Historical Skills
Maps and Mapping
Weather, Climate
Science Skills

The lists have been placed in Section 3 of these guidelines for convenience when planning topics. It can be seen that each of the lists contains a table of skills and that each skill is subdivided into three stages. Very broadly, these three stages follow the stages of development outlined by Piaget. It is important to note that:

1. Each stage extends and builds upon the one before.

2. Children pass through the stages in the order 1, 2, 3 though the rate at which they pass through them varies between individuals.

3. Age is no guide to stage. The stage of development will vary from child to child and also from skill to skill for the same child.

Basically the stages could be described in this way.

Stage 1

Transition from pre-operational to concrete operational thought. Thought is closely associated with physical action and observation. Developing the ability to manipulate things mentally.

Stage 2

Concrete operational thought is well established. Mental manipulations are becoming more established and powerful. Increasing ability to handle variables and solve problems. Everything is still rooted in real, physical experiences.

Stage 3

Transition from concrete operational thought to formal operational thought. Developing power to think about the abstract, to hypothesise, to generalise, to draw conclusions.

Generally the formal operational ability will not be fully apparent until the age of 13 although some progress in that direction should be expected at primary school.

When planning a topic, the teacher can refer to these lists of skills; knowing the children concerned and after having referred to their records, the teacher can select skills appropriate to the topic for teaching to the children. All the skills should be attempted over the school year.

Each of the skill lists is quite straightforward. Each skill is numbered and this number is used when planning. (See Section 3.) There is one exception to this. It will be seen that the skill lists for Weather/Climate are not numbered.

In the case of Weather/Climate, the list comprises aspects of Weather/Climate which the child should be taught during each of its three stages of development. The teacher should ensure that each of the items listed under a particular stage are taught during that stage of the child's development;

Broadly speaking this means:

Stage 1 — Infant
Stage 2 — Lower Junior
Stage 3 — Upper Junior

GENERAL, SOCIAL, PHYSICAL SKILLS AND ATTITUDES

Certain fundamental skills have been identified which do not spring from any particular subject discipline but which are basic to learning and are vital to later stages of learning and indeed to adult life. It is, for example, most important that children should develop good work habits, that they should be able to approach and solve appropriate problems, that they should be able to reason logically and critically analyse.

It is just as important that they can co-operate and work with others, that they are curious, that they develop open-mindedness and that their attitude towards themselves is good.

These skills and attitudes are open-ended. Their development is never complete, even in adulthood. Education has been described as a 'road to travel' and certainly where the skills and attitudes under discussion in this section are concerned there is always a farther horizon beckoning the learner. We cannot say, certainly at the primary level, that such skills and attitudes have been attained, but we should continuously seek to develop them.

These skills and attitudes are therefore not sub-divided into stages and numbered as the others are. It is assumed that *all* integrated studies work will be so planned to provide opportunities for their development. The teacher will be asked to assess the extent of their development topic by topic . . .

At Starvale, therefore, the belief is clear that topic work requires the acquisition by pupils of skills and concepts within a content framework which combines subject disciplines into an integrated whole. Examples of these skills and concepts, and how they develop, are given in the next section.

(v) Questions of progression

Here there are two main areas to explore: how Starvale identifies and conceptualises progress in the skills it has isolated as critical to the primary phase of education; and how records of pupils' progress are kept. This next extract shows a selection of important skills across a range of subject disciplines; these skills are thought to develop at the infant (Stage I), lower junior (Stage II) and upper junior (Stage III) levels.

Recording pupils' progress must be tailored to take account of the rationale of topic work adopted by the school. This is clearly shown in the extract which follows:

Starvale staff handbook, Extract F (adapted and abridged)

We must of course keep records . . . for each teacher's use and for

Starvale staff handbook, Extract E

HISTORICAL SKILLS IN INTEGRATED STUDIES

NO.	SKILL	STAGE I	STAGE II	STAGE III
1	Awareness of time and sequence	Observe; respond to: ask questions about — the 'oldness' of objects; mementoes; pictures; personal events related to the child's own experience — Me — parents — grandparents; and before it. Help to construct simple life lines and family charts.	Able to identify some 'concrete' objects, e.g. coins, cars, as being older than others. Place objects in a simple logical order. Use and construct simple time charts of his own history and other immediate experiences, in conjunction with pictures and vocabulary.	Respond to and recognise selected 'time cues', e.g. museum objects; family or personal mementoes, pictures of a wide variety of historical 'stereotypes', e.g. dinosaurs, Concorde, Guy Fawkes etc., in order to sequence events within a broad, very simple framework.
2	Awareness of working with evidence	As above and observing, in conjunction with an old map, 'old' buildings in the neighbourhood.	Relate old maps of the locality to old buildings. Work with readily tabulated information, e.g. trade directories, census material, etc., to make comparisons between 'Then' and 'Now'.	Recognise objects in the locality etc. as clues to 'the past'. Deduce how old objects were used from detailed clues, and empathise with the people who used them. Examine evidence, distinguish between legend and history, exaggeration, truth, and falsehood as 'is it true?' 'how do we know?'

3	Terminology	Use 'then'; 'now'; 'new'; 'old'; 'very old'.	Use 'recent'; 'modern'; 'ancient'; 'old'. Acquaintance with terms such as BC; AD; King; Ruler, etc.	Use the vocabulary of historical investigation and simple terminology, e.g. 'ancestors', 'biased', 'hearsay', 'incident', 'sympathy', 'viewpoint', leading to 'council', 'civilisation', etc.
4	Evaluation		Begins to make comparisons and look for differences, e.g. between historical personalities 'then and now'.	Begins to connect events in a very simple fashion in terms of cause and effect. Begins to think about events not only from a present-day viewpoint but from the viewpoint of people living at the time. Begins through discussion to be aware of totally opposed view of the same historical person. Begins to make inferences and give simple judgements, e.g. reasons for connecting persons and events based on details of a story.

HISTORICAL SKILLS IN INTEGRATED STUDIES (contd.)

NO. SKILL	STAGE I	STAGE II	STAGE III
5 Communication (Investigatory)	Observes, asks questions, listens to famous stories and writes about them.	Observes, in order to identify and describe, the characteristics of objects, pictures, etc., and frames questions about them. Able to extract simple information from reference books, photographs, etc.	Adductive — begins to put together an idea of an object, e.g. bridge, or a process, e.g. Civil War, from a number of details, e.g. about bridges or the English Civil War in Derbyshire, from a variety of sources, referring back to those sources as authority for statement.

SCIENCE SKILLS IN INTEGRATED STUDIES

1. For further development of Stages I, II and III see L.F. Ennever and W. Harlen, 'With objectives in mind', in W. Harlen, *Guide to Science 5–13: a formative evaluation* (Macmillan, London, 1975), pp. 59 ff.
2. For an index of content see 'Learning through Science', *Guide to Science 5–13*, pp. 34–65.

NO.	SKILL	STAGE I	STAGE II	STAGE III
1	Observing/Exploring: Enquiring	Exploring sights, sounds, smells, textures, tastes	Simple investigation of materials of the environment to test e.g. strength. Understanding basic principles through use of representational models	Detailed study of habitat, e.g. school grounds or 'natural' habitat
2	Ordering of thoughts/Logical thinking	Recording findings in writing; block graphs	Devising own classification and keys for identification	Mapping distribution and keeping records of seasonal change from observation
3	Posing questions; devising experiments	Finding answers to simple problems by investigation	Awareness of variables and need to control them	Devising controlled experiments with one variable
4	Communicating	Correct scientific use of new words, model making	Construction of models to scale	Choice of most appropriate means of communicating results

SCIENCE SKILLS IN INTEGRATED STUDIES (contd.)

NO.	SKILL	STAGE I	STAGE II	STAGE III
5	Appreciating patterns and relationships	Forming a broad idea of variation in living things Encourage awareness that size and shape depend on position of observer, e.g. distance, three dimensions and perspective	Awareness of sequence of change in nature and inter-dependence among living things Understanding that properties of materials influence their use, e.g. glass for windows, types of clothing	Relationships between different local areas, e.g. industry, homes and also local and worldwide
6	Concluding, interpreting findings critically	Suggests guided logical conclusions	Draws conclusion from available evidence Check findings for error	Ability to draw unbiased conclusion from observation

MATHEMATICAL SKILLS IN INTEGRATED STUDIES

NO.	SKILL	STAGE I	STAGE II	STAGE III
1	Pure number	Comparisons — more/less many/few Calculations using basic four rules	Creating own census Interpreting graphs Using simple fractions	Using published census material, i.e. population; transport; temperature Findings: average fractions percentages ratios Random counting
2	Measuring	Size — big/small Arbitrary units — spans Area — using arbitrary shapes	Accurate standard measures Perimeters Area — using squares of standard measurements Using callipers	Calculating areas Accurate perimeters Scale Surveying Quadrants; transects
3	Sets	Colour — size — shape	Features, e.g. legs, leaves	Complicated classification Making own keys
4	Graphing	Tally charts; pictorial graphs; bar graphs	Bar, stick, line graphs	As Stage II — using larger numbers, pie graphs
5	Timing	By counting	By stopwatch and clock	Creating own timing devices

These are the skills relevant in integrated studies and are intended to complement, *not* replace maths teaching.

passing on with the child through the school, thereby ensuring continuity and progression. Samples of the record sheets are attached . . .

The record sheet marked 'B' is to be used for each child during school life from Middle Infant . . .

Sheet B is designed to provide a progressive record of

(a) Topics studied by the child.
(b) Stages of development in skills.
(c) Skills practised.
(d) Distant places covered.
(e) Aspects of weather covered.

It should be completed for each child at the end of each topic . . .
This system of evaluation and record-keeping is designed to be as brief but useful as possible. It is in existence to assist us to:

(a) Plan our work to be effective.
(b) Knowing each child's stage of development, match the task to the child.
(c) Ensure that we can monitor the progress of each child progressively and continuously.

Sheet B is shown on page 131.

(vi) Questions of professional development and accountability

The handbook provides a limited amount of information only about the professional development of teachers at Starvale. Obviously, these teachers have gained both from compiling the handbook and from using it, and no doubt from the consultations which led up to it. Beyond this we can tell little.

Similarly, there is no indication of widespread use of outside personnel from the community in topic teaching; but the link between school and the community has been hinted at in the extracts (see section (i) above).

The handbook itself provides a point of reference for interested parties: those in other schools, support agencies and advisers.

The single most important shaft of light that the handbook sheds on these questions is the emphasis it puts on teachers' own self-evaluation. The following quotation gives the flavour:

RECORD OF PROGRESS IN SKILLS [MIDDLE INFANTS ONWARDS (B)]

NAME _____

	SKILL																																			
	TOPIC TITLE / DATE																																				
HISTORICAL	Time/Sequence	1																																			
	Working with evidence	2																																			
	Terminology	3																																			
	Evaluation	4																																			
	Communication	5																																			
SCIENTIFIC	Observing/Exploring	1																																			
	Logical thinking	2																																			
	Questions/Experiments	3																																			
	Communicating	4																																			
	Patterns/Relationships	5																																			
	Concluding	6																																			
MATHEMATICAL	Pure number	1																																			
	Measuring	2																																			
	Sets	3																																			
	Graphing	4																																			
	Timing	5																																			
LANGUAGE	Listening	1																																			
	Talking	2																																			
	Comprehension	3																																			
	Writing	4																																			
	Reference skills	5																																			
	Reference-book skills	6																																			
	Library skills	7																																			
	Types of writing	8																																			
MAPS AND MAPPING	Position/Orientation	1																																			
	Map symbols	2																																			
	Map scale	3																																			
	Map perspective	4																																			
	Map purpose	5																																			
	Map drawing	6																																			
	Map reading	7																																			
	Map interpretation	8																																			
	Map style	9																																			

Starvale staff handbook, Extract G

Under *'TEACHER'S EVALUATION'*, *at the end of the topic, the teacher should write a few brief, honest notes concerning organisational matters. The idea of this brief section is to encourage the teacher to think positively about the topic completed and to write down these thoughts. This will assist in the organisation of the next topic.*

THE CASE OF STARVALE

Earlier, Starvale was described as having an 'articulated rationale' for topic work. This rationale has now been substantially illustrated. The differences between the case of Dovecote Mill and the case of Starvale are obvious and deep-rooted. The two cases exemplify the ends of a spectrum in approaches to topic work; other case-studied schools fell between these two extremes in the progress they had made towards evolving effective approaches to topic work. Neither school has a monopoly of right or wrong procedures. Since each school is unique, to talk in such terms is futile. The two cases serve to encourage the reader to come to grips with the main themes and questions discussed.

5

Preparing Topics

THE NATURAL HISTORY OF A TOPIC

This chapter begins where the previous one finished, with a rationale for topic work. Strictly, it begins with the translation of that rationale into classroom intentions and objectives. To prepare effectively, some guiding principles of this kind for the planning process are essential to the teacher. If one message of the chapter on curriculum management has been that conscious decisions, based on articulated educational goals, need to be made at a school level when topic work is contemplated, then it has to be admitted that topics are, in individual classroom practice, more likely to evolve. For this reason it is pertinent to describe the emergence of a topic as its 'natural history'. This natural history is exemplified in case-study conversation between one caseworker and the head of a six-teacher rural primary school nestling six miles from a bustling market town in a fold in the agriculturally rich woldland of a northern county.

Extract from a tape-recorded conversation with the head teacher (MD) of Denton Primary School (place-names have been changed)

CSW. Now, Martin, you're headmaster at Denton Primary School and the reason we've come up to talk to you today is because one of the things you've been doing recently is a topic based on Kirby village: an environmental topic. But what is so interesting about this topic is the way it came about and in particular the amount of preparation and the kind of preparation that went on. I've got in front of me here a booklet which was produced by a small group of wildlife enthusiasts in the Kirby area, and I'm going to ask you a bit about this operation that you went on for six months in the area. Can you tell us how your own interest in Kirby came about?

MD. Yes. The farmer, in fact, invited the school to come along and have a look at his land and to see what we could find, and I thought this would be quite a challenge and with the group of friends I decided that it might be an idea to first of all involve grown-ups and consequently we had several meetings and met at Kirby and began in January.

CSW. Let me ask you to tell us where Kirby is in relation, first of all, to the county as a whole and then in relation to the school?

MD. Yes. Kirby is about three miles from Leck and approximately three miles from Denton so it's between Leck and Denton and it lies in a valley. It has a derelict railway line running through it and mixed farmland all round it.

CSW. So we've got a picture then of a woldland farm and a small village with a village school. But at the moment we are interested in what our small group of naturalists, of whom you were a member, actually did on the farm of Mr Smith in Kirby. Can you describe some of the activities which you carried out?

MD. Yes. We looked at our expertise that we had available to us and we decided that several members would look at the railway line because they felt it would be an interesting area to study the bird life and the territories there that the migrants were forming in the early spring. Other members decided to look at the snail populations along the railway line while others spent quite a lot of time looking at birds of prey and different mammals on the opposite side of the railway line: there happened to be a road that divides the farm in half.

CSW. Perhaps that's a good moment to break off and try and describe the terrain of the farm. Can you tell us a little bit about what the farm looks like and what the study area looks like?

MD. Yes. As I said before, the village lies at the bottom of a valley. The railway line runs along from the western side of the farm and the River Lud starts from beneath the railway line and the railway line has lots of embankments and cuttings. At the end of the railway line, as far as the farm's concerned, is a tunnel which happened to be the longest railway tunnel in the county. To the north of the railway line are lots of glacial valleys that are used for grazing and then where the road happens to be that's on a ridge. On the opposite side of that there are more valleys and woodland.

CSW. And what was interesting about this survey was, in fact, that the farm divides rather neatly into a number of small habitats.

134

You've mentioned the railway line and there was an area of birchwood and an area of ashwood. That's right, isn't it?

MD. That's right.

CSW. And when you got going and started to look at some of these things you did something on a study of owls and pellets, I seem to recall from what you were telling me earlier. Can you tell me something about studying owls and pellets?

MD. Yes. On the farm we found that many of the owl species were present, barn owl, tawny owl, short-eared owl and little owl, and we were able to find signs of these birds in particular places. For example, we were able to observe the barn owl in some derelict RAF buildings. We were able to observe the tawny owl in the woodland, and in the open farmland we were able to see short-eared owls and little owls; through careful examination we were able to find their pellets and examine them and this led to a greater study of the mammal population in that area and we were able to identify the food sources of these birds and the percentage taken of a variety of mammals.

CSW. Yes. In the little booklet that the group produced at the end of this study, a very attractive little booklet with delightful drawings (I understand the group, in fact, recruited an artist specially to illustrate the book), it actually gives the percentages of some of these animals in the owl food.

MD. Yes it does.

CSW. We've got here a bank vole, about 7 per cent of the food this owl took was bank vole, 25 per cent field vole, 9 per cent wood mouse, 15 per cent rat, a very small amount of rabbit food taken. So, an intricate study of that particular bird, and reading on in the book I discovered, too, that you looked at the mammal life of this woodland. What kind of mammals turned up in the woodland? Some you have identified from the pellets; were there any other interesting ones?

MD. Well, quite a wide variety really. They needed looking for. If we hadn't found the owl pellets I think we would have been at a total loss; we were able to observe grey squirrels and several of the voles as we were walking along but we were unable to find any places where the house mouse and the wood mouse happened to be: they were in the pellets, so obviously they were around in the environment, but there was nothing really that surprised us. Most of the mammals were there from the pipistrelle bat to stoat, weasel, badger and fox. They were there. We were very fortunate and with using the owl pellets and the observers around who would spot things we were able to draw quite a complex picture of life around.

CSW. Yes. I've been reading another section of the book: there was quite a detailed study of the bird life along this railway track. Now, as I understand it, the railway track, the lines have now been removed, but there is a kind of double hedge all the way along and in places it is an embankment and in places it runs higher than the surrounding farmland, and what was interesting from this study was that the bird populations along that piece of suitable habitat were very dense compared to their normal density on a piece of woodland, let us say. So clearly the farm is providing a haven for wildlife in the area. So this was the starting point then of an interest which consumed about six months of the half dozen or so people in this group of naturalists. But perhaps we can turn our attention away from natural history for a minute and talk about the railway line itself. What was the railway line used for and how long has it been derelict, do you think?

MD. Well, the railway line went through Kirby from the county town to Leck. It was a single-track railway line and it was used very frequently by the farm. In fact, I was only talking to the farmer the other day who feels he would have great use for that railway line right now but at the time, about thirty years ago, the farm used the railway line to import cattle for fattening. He also used it for the main crop of the farm, which happened to be potatoes. It is one of the very first farms in the county, in fact, to grow potatoes. He used to use the railway line to transport his potatoes and his other crops.

CSW. The platform is actually in the farmyard, or the remains of the farmyard?

MD. That's right. In fact, the farm still retains the station and the station house and also the shed that was on the platform which is now used as a chapel. So it's still being used these days and they still use the station for loading their lorries. It's still in good use really, it's in remarkably good condition.

CSW. I think you described what it was like to walk along the railway line and into the tunnel: although the tunnel was bricked up some time ago there is still a doorway which is accessible?

MD. Yes. The station is at one end of the farm's railway line and the tunnel is at the other, and the distance between the station and the tunnel is about a mile; as you walk along the railway line you are aware of a change in environment as you walk towards the tunnel. You are aware of embankments at one moment and then cuttings at another. And all the time there is a change in the amount of vegetation around you. And the sides of the railway tracks are still there because where the tracks have been it's still bare although it's 20 years since the tracks were there. But the excitement comes really as the railway lines twist. The old track twists and turns towards the tunnel and you are aware then of a gaping hole at the end of the embankments which is the tunnel. There is a small opening in it and it's from there that a lot, particularly children anyway, found great excitement because there are stalactites and stalagmites formed within there, and signs of bats, and there's still a lot of soot left inside the tunnel. It's a very dirty place; children love it.

CSW. I can remember going through it myself and there's a point in the tunnel, isn't there, when you can't see either end, there's a moment when you are in total darkness and you just reach out, if your torch fails to work at the vital moment and everything appears to be solid black. I'm reading now from the booklet and one paragraph says the village church is dedicated to St Martin which was erected in 1882 at a cost of £1,337. The village school predates the church by some eight years and was enlarged in 1889 to accommodate 60 pupils. That seems like a good moment to describe your school.

MD. Well, in fact, in 1969 the children from Leck transferred to Denton, so there's a direct link there. In fact, we're still able to find some of the old books that we used in our resources here that were used at Leck School. But Denton is a primary school and it has, at the moment, 90 children on roll; and it is made up of four classes: an infant class which includes reception children and first- and second-year infants, and then a first-year junior class, a second- and part third-year junior class and a fourth year with some third year in it.

CSW. You told me earlier on that there was an arrangement with a neighbouring school by which you share and pool some expertise. Could you say a word or two about that?

MD. Yes. We share our resources with a school at Thetford. Thetford is a reasonably new school and has a fully equipped gym whereas we have very few facilities in that area but, at the same time, we have a kiln and we are able to offer other curriculum developments when we decide to come together. We discuss these with the two teachers and we decide that Denton perhaps will go to Thetford to use their gym whereas Thetford children should come here to do pottery.

CSW. That's interesting because this is an unusual sort of arrangement and it's quite a good point to cue in some information about this topic itself. You did the topic based on the Kirby village and you took up the information which you had gained by being a member of this naturalists' group, and so a lot of the preparation for this work was actually done some six months earlier in your own spare time. Then you had a reciprocal arrangement with your neighbouring school and the project got off the ground. Can you tell us something about this particular piece of topic work?

MD. Yes. We decided that it would be a useful thing to come together and share experience through environmental studies. It seemed obvious to me that all this work that had gone on at Leck could be used and adapted for primary children and so I discussed with the head teacher the possibilities. Consequently we decided that it would be best to bring the children together and to look at some slides that were taken by the group and this had the effect of encouraging the children to think about Kirby and to think about their own villages in relation to Kirby and look at what the facilities were at Kirby compared to their own village. Leck is a very, very small place. It had a very large population a hundred years ago but now has only a very few families whereas both Denton and Thetford are growing villages. From the films the children were able to see most of the areas that they would be visiting and the teachers were able to discuss various parts of Leck through the slides.

CSW. Tell me how the six weeks of the topic were actually organised?

MD. Yes. It was, in fact, six days out of six weeks, one day each week we joined together and went to Leck. The first visit we all stayed together and explored Leck as a group. A rather large group, but we decided it was best to explore the various areas, the various aspects, the various environments that were available to the children, and the only thing that we said to them was to be aware, to observe and to think about areas that they found interesting, but generally to give them an overview of the whole environment, and so the first day was spent in the morning looking at the railway line, looking at the station, exploring the tunnel and looking at the environment around the railway line. The afternoon we spent walking through the woodland of the valleys and so we visited three woods, we looked at the trout pond, the trout stream and while we were specialising in woodland and the railway line we were also looking at the farmland all around us.

We just cannot get away from that at all. So it was the farmland, the railway line and the woodland and the children were given the opportunity to see what was available, and a few children already were making their minds up what they were going to do next week, whereas a lot of them needed some discussion, which was done during the course of the next week.

CSW. Right, so in the second week, then, you got them to do some kind of group work?

MD. That's right. The children decided for themselves for the second week the areas in which they would like to study. Now, some children decided they would like to find out as much as they could about badgers because there was a very large badger sett there, but other children decided they would like to find out about the history of the railway line, the function of the railway line, so they were given the opportunity, while others decided they would like to spend some time in the tunnel and others, a small group, also surveyed the crops being used on the farm. So that was during the course of the next week and on the following visit that is exactly what happened. And so a group of children became an expert in a small area of a farm.

CSW. That went on for several weeks then?

MD. That went on for a couple of weeks where they were able to follow through their research and to discover as much as they could about their specialism.

CSW. And what did they do with the information once they'd actually got it?

MD. They shared that information then with the groups who were specialising in other areas, so consequently the third week was spent with the children who specialised in the badger sett leading the group of children who were specialising in the tunnel, and then that worked the other way in the afternoon, where the children who specialised in the tunnel were able to play tapes of steam engines to the children who had been researching into the badgers, and they were able to tell them the history of the railway line, the sort of engines that would travel through the tunnel and any animals that they found, rats and things, you know, dead rabbits in the tunnel.

CSW. They took the tape recorders out with them?

MD. They did, yes.

CSW. So they were learning on the ground the whole time and this took place around April time?

MD. That's right.

CSW. So not necessarily the best period of the year for weather but they braved the elements?

MD. Yes. Well the weather is all part of the area and we found that although perhaps it might have been reasonably cold they were still able to cope with working, and it didn't interfere with anything that we did, and one group of children were using surveying apparatus, clinometers, various other things to work out the volumes of earth removed from cuttings, and it still seemed to work quite successfully.

CSW. Yes. Let's take that up because there were two kinds of outcome from this environmental topic which were unusual and very interesting. One was that there was a lot of mathematics work that came out of it, and you've mentioned a little bit of that, and the second was that there were some musical things that came out of it. But let's start with the mathematics. Quite unusual to end up with maths from an environmental topic?

MD. I don't know. We don't seem to end up with a lot of maths that comes out of environmental studies. You can't seem to separate maths from much that was done. From just the sheer shape of the tunnel entrance, which itself is very interesting — it's not a normal shape, it's narrower at the bottom than you would expect. We used our maths because the children asked questions that needed maths to answer it. We talked about navvies and their ability manually to move very, very difficult surfaces, and the chalk there is not easy to remove. We discussed how much had to be removed and why it was necessary for railway lines to be flat, level. The children then posed the questions and the teachers directed them to a certain amount of research necessary, which meant maths, and they used maths to draw their own conclusions; we just gave them the necessary information and they then were able to work out for themselves, and so consequently maths was involved tremendously in everything we did . . . The children would estimate how deep a badger sett would be but also they could work out the size of the badger from the hole; they had to count the holes, they had to work out how far the outlets were away from the sett. They also measured how high the scratches up the tree happened to be so they could work out how far the badger could reach up a tree, and gain some information about badgers' physical make-up. It was all around us.

CSW. Yes, I think that's an interesting observation, because so often when we talk about topic work people talk about it in a subject-specific kind of way, and clearly you were very interdisciplinary here and that in itself is interesting. And they shared: the children who were involved in the topic shared what they found with other children in the school. They took the infants out on an afternoon's ramble to show them what they found.

MD. Yes. We thought it would be nice if the older juniors, after all their hard work, if they could, in fact, lead a group and so have the opportunity of taking the infants, and this they did. Again the children were allowed to be the specialists in their areas; the infants had a guided tour around the farm and they were led by the junior children who were able to outline all their findings to the infants, and both thoroughly enjoyed themselves.

CSW. If you had to sum up, what do you think is the value of this kind of work? What would you say that it contributed to the life of the school and to the education of the child?

MD. Oh, it contributed in many ways. I suppose, I'm not sure if I'm going to put this in the right sort of order, this is thinking out of the top of my head, but certainly socially it had tremendous benefits, not so much between the children at the same school but because the children had to share and to work with children that they hadn't met before so there's a certain amount of social behaviour. It gave the children the opportunity to develop their mathematical thinking from problems that they had evolved themselves. Unlike the questions that are set in their textbooks or perhaps that a teacher would set, the problems as far as maths were concerned developed through the children's own experience, a need to know. They found that they needed a piece of information, they didn't have the answer, the teacher didn't have the answer, the teacher might be able to point them in the right direction as to the tools required and the method to be used and they worked it out together, so, therefore, that was a very good experience for the children, it was maths with a reason, maths with meaning. There was a lot of recording, tremendous English came out of it, and as we said earlier music came out of it, too, in that the children put music tunes to some of their programmes that they wrote. Again the children were encouraged to form an hypothesis of various parts of the study and they had to think very seriously about badgers, when they were likely to come out, and they would ask questions and also try to prove those questions. For example, if working with the badgers there were a lot of holes some children wanted to know were all the holes used? The answer, of course, was, well, 'we don't really know'. How best to find out? So we put sticks in the holes so that, *in fact, the badger could push them out. They were not in there so that the badger couldn't get in or out but they were put in carefully; by doing that the children were able to see sticks being knocked out and their questions were starting to be answered through their own thinking. So it was a variety of things really and I can't pinpoint any one particular educational aspect that the children benefited from. It cuts across the whole curriculum.*

CSW. Well, one aspect of that curriculum that has been mentioned several times is music, and the children actually put together some words and some music and worked on it in their own time, and what we are going to do now is, in fact, play out our tape by letting the audience hear some of that music.

In the foregoing case extract the evolution of the topic consists of four stages: acquired knowledge at an adult level, insight concerning the potential of this knowledge around a theme for exploitation as a pupils' topic, discovery learning by the pupils, and exploitation of pupil discoveries in various multi-disciplinary directions through the professional judgement of the teachers involved. The potential of this project theme was seen in prospect; its potential learning outcomes became obvious in retrospect.

This, though a recurrent form of natural history for a project, is not the only one. Nor is it the commonest. The most frequent is hinted at in this caseworker's notes about two studied teachers in a large primary school set in the suburbs of a market town:

The school was in the early stages of formulating a topic-work scheme and there were no agreed sets of aims for topic work. Despite this, both teachers said they formulated their own sets of aims, though they differed slightly in the direction these took.

Mrs A placed the emphasis on widening the children's knowledge, creating an enthusiasm for learning, and teaching them the skills necessary for research: using a library, an index and a dictionary, skimming and scanning.

Mrs B put the emphasis on concepts, skills and attitudes, decided upon according to the nature of the topic . . .

When it came to the actual planning of the topic both teachers reported that they began with a flow diagram.

This terse piece of reporting leads us back to examine some of the questions we raised about preparations for topic teaching in chapter 3, and forward into a more detailed analysis of teachers' practice on this theme.

TYPOLOGIES AND EMPHASES IN TOPIC PLANNING

We begin with two sets of questions previously outlined in chapter 3.

Questions about intentions and objectives

As a classroom teacher, what are your aims, intentions and objectives for topic teaching?

How do you decide upon these for any given topic?

Do you know precisely the main

> **items of knowledge**
> **practical and social skills**
> **concepts and ideas**

you hope to impart through any given topic?

Questions about planning procedures

Do you have a systematic approach to preparation, an order in which to prepare yourself, your resources, your pupils and the classroom?

Do you commit your planning to paper?

How long would you expect to spend in preparation for an unfamiliar topic?

When is this preparation carried out?

Do you commit this planning to paper?

Do you pass these plans to anyone else for comment?

Do you use these plans again for other classes, or destroy them when the topic is over?

As we have seen from the brief extract above, teachers tend to divide into those who emphasise content and knowledge of information (the majority) and those who emphasise conceptual learning. This is a recurrent dichotomy in our case studies and, one suspects from more general conversation, across the profession. But both sets of teachers plan similarly, often beginning their planning from a flow chart. These charts require, therefore, some scrutiny.

Figures 5.1–5.5 are examples of flow charts culled from our case-studied schools. Flow charts represent the most ubiquitous planning procedure; but how they relate to intentions and objectives often has to be deduced.

Figure 5.1: Flow diagram of a study of the period 1936–53 based on the ITV series 'How we used to live'; 2nd-year juniors in a downtown urban area. Two terms' work.

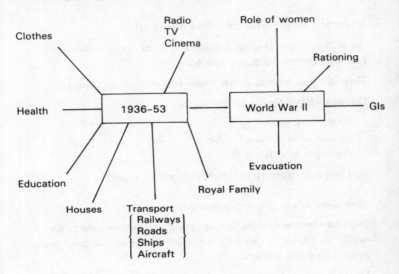

These flow diagrams in Figures 5.1–5.5 represent the five typologies which recur in the cases of our case study, and it is instructive to look at them in a little more detail.

The topic in Figure 5.1 is characterised by data: each branch of the diagram represents *information about* the central topic or theme. Figure 5.2, which deals with a topic for very young children, is largely about *activities*: looking, collecting, visiting. With older pupils the word 'activity' might be replaced by the description 'skill', for example, accurate measuring or weighing. In the pollution topic outlined in Figure 5.3 most items in the five content branches suggest a *problem-solving or analytical approach* in which pupils will be required to guess or hypothesise, to experiment, to deduce and conclude. The fourth approach is a *conceptual* one, in which it is ideas, and the connections between them, that form the axes of the diagram.

Each of these four figures represents a way of reviewing what might be included in a topic. Each represents, too, a way of thinking about the intellectual demand that a topic makes upon the pupils. Which method is adopted tells us something about the teacher's underlying rationale, philosophies and emphases: to impart information,

Figure 5.2: Flow diagram of a study of the topic 'Wheels' in a reception class of a small rural primary school.

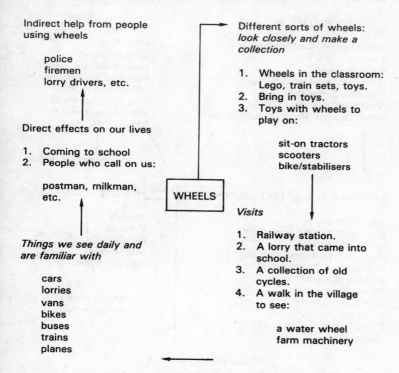

Indirect help from people using wheels

    police
    firemen
    lorry drivers, etc.

Direct effects on our lives

1. Coming to school
2. People who call on us:

    postman, milkman, etc.

Things we see daily and are familiar with

    cars
    lorries
    vans
    bikes
    buses
    trains
    planes

WHEELS

Different sorts of wheels: *look closely and make a collection*

1. Wheels in the classroom: Lego, train sets, toys.
2. Bring in toys.
3. Toys with wheels to play on:

    sit-on tractors
    scooters
    bike/stabilisers

Visits

1. Railway station.
2. A lorry that came into school.
3. A collection of old cycles.
4. A walk in the village to see:

    a water wheel
    farm machinery

to help children experience the world, to encourage questions and investigation or to help with concept acquisition. Thus intentions and planning procedures are inextricably intertwined.

Theoretically, perhaps, topic planning would be more effective if teachers were to make not one flow diagram but *several*. Each one would be aimed at a particular aspect of the topic: its data, its potential for useful activities and skills, its potential for higher-level thinking and for concept development. These flow diagrams would link up; and the planning would cease to be flat and arid and would become three-dimensional and living. In practice we did not find a single example of such an approach to the use of flow diagrams. Rather, if teachers were aware of a problem here, they resorted to one of two ploys, the first being less effective than the second.

Figure 5.3: Flow diagram of a study of the topic 'Pollution' in the fourth-year primary class of a busy market-town school.

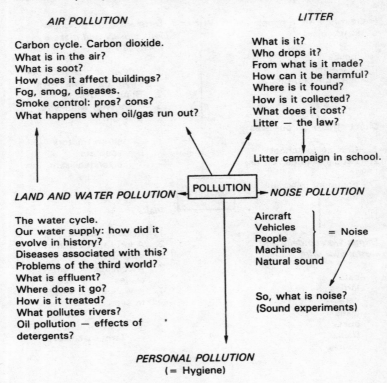

AIR POLLUTION

Carbon cycle. Carbon dioxide.
What is in the air?
What is soot?
How does it affect buildings?
Fog, smog, diseases.
Smoke control: pros? cons?
What happens when oil/gas run out?

LITTER

What is it?
Who drops it?
From what is it made?
How can it be harmful?
Where is it found?
How is it collected?
What does it cost?
Litter — the law?

Litter campaign in school.

LAND AND WATER POLLUTION ← POLLUTION → *NOISE POLLUTION*

The water cycle.
Our water supply: how did it evolve in history?
Diseases associated with this?
Problems of the third world?
What is effluent?
Where does it go?
How is it treated?
What pollutes rivers?
Oil pollution — effects of detergents?

Aircraft
Vehicles
People
Machines
Natural sound
} = Noise

So, what is noise?
(Sound experiments)

PERSONAL POLLUTION
(= Hygiene)

Why do we keep clean?
How?
From what germs?
What are the results of NOT keeping clean?
Have people always worried about cleanliness?

The first ploy was to attempt a *single* flow diagram which contained several levels of approach. Figure 5.5 here well illustrates this method. Content is outlined under the heading 'map work' and implicit elsewhere. Activities are suggested and implied in 'further research' and 'comparison of habitats'. 'Change' and 'conservation' are concepts ripe for exploration under this topic heading. But the diagram itself lacks coherence and the links between parts, represented by arrows, tend to defy easy definition despite the fact that the gist of the planning is clear.

Figure 5.4: A flow or target diagram of a study of the concept 'Man', carried out over four primary years. Each ring on the target can be put at the centre of a 'new' target and similarly dissected.

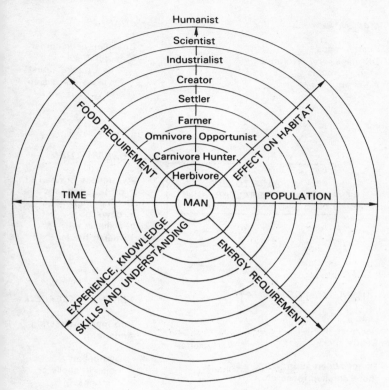

Source: Peter Cast, *All the years round* (Nottinghamshire LEA, 1979), p. 20. This book was compiled for use in a large urban primary school in a fairly deprived setting which was studied during the project.

By contrast, the second ploy is to abandon the flow diagram as a planning medium and to use some more extended form of statement. This is illustrated by the following extract from a staff handbook gathered from one of our case-studied schools:

Figure 5.5: Flow diagram of a topic about Gibraltar Point Nature Reserve: a place to live. Carried out by a fourth-year junior class from a large suburban school as part of its work for the summer term.

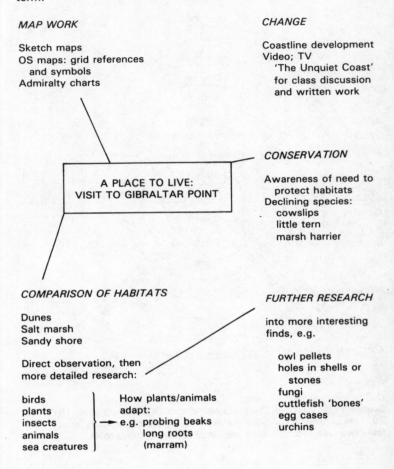

MAP WORK

Sketch maps
OS maps: grid references
  and symbols
Admiralty charts

CHANGE

Coastline development
Video; TV
  'The Unquiet Coast'
    for class discussion
    and written work

A PLACE TO LIVE:
VISIT TO GIBRALTAR POINT

CONSERVATION

Awareness of need to
  protect habitats
Declining species:
  cowslips
  little tern
  marsh harrier

COMPARISON OF HABITATS

Dunes
Salt marsh
Sandy shore

Direct observation, then
more detailed research:

birds
plants
insects
animals
sea creatures

How plants/animals
adapt:
e.g. probing beaks
    long roots
    (marram)

FURTHER RESEARCH

into more interesting
finds, e.g.

owl pellets
holes in shells or
  stones
fungi
cuttlefish 'bones'
egg cases
urchins

Extract from staff handbook of Blaydon CP School

ENVIRONMENTAL SYLLABUS — FIRST-YEAR JUNIORS

The young child is generally very self-orientated unless he or she has come from a largish family. Infant children are learning to fit into a school society and accept some adaptations to their behaviour pattern.

148

By the time the children reach first-year junior level (or when they have reached some fluency in reading) they should be ready to be made aware of the needs of others outside their own circle of familiar faces. Generally then we should take each opportunity of pointing out the ways of life of other peoples in the world and of people in the past. In other words — *to widen their horizons*. As each environmental topic unfolds, there may be numerous such occasions.

As at infant level, children should be encouraged to talk about how things look, feel, smell, taste — how heavy, large, rough, attractive, unattractive they are. Children can be expected to write about their impressions and show them in picture and model form using many different media. In addition *simple study skills are introduced* to help children to clarify their findings.

Some study skills to introduce

Mapping. Don't be afraid to use maps although it is a difficult concept for a young child to understand. Wall maps usually arouse a lot of interest, especially if they are of an area which children can associate with and provided that they are not expected to cope with too much, too soon.

Use plenty of sketch maps of their own area — local roads and street maps. Let children use their own symbols and show them how to set out a key.

Plans — rooms and playground etc., from the air (not to scale).

Co-ordinates — simple cross-referencing (as in 'Battleships and Cruisers'). Perhaps by making up a treasure map?

Reference books. At the beginning children can only recognise the difference between books by the picture on the cover or perhaps the title.

1. Begin with class discussions — how to recognise a reference book, how is it different from story books? What is it for?

2. Children could be shown a selection of really short reference books suited to their ability and also given practical exercises, e.g. a few simple questions to answer orally and by using a simple questionnaire — with no indication of which page the answer is on. When children understand how a simple reference book can be used then written answers could be used.

3. Use simple dictionaries in preparation for introduction to

pictorial reference-type volumes (e.g. *Black's Children's Encyclopaedia, Our World Encyclopaedia*).

Exercises can be devised to be conducted in groups. The answers may be copied verbatim, but encourage children to provide answers in their own words. (This can be a guide to the child's understanding of reading content.)

The School Library. At the beginning of this syllabus there is a chart to explain the school library colour-coding system. The same system is used at both schools to give continuity. Some group work in the library — with a teacher — will be needed so that the children will know which section to go for to find a book on a certain subject. (It may be a while before children are ready to take this step on their own.)

History time-line. We have decided that it would be a good idea to have a simple time-line in each classroom, all the time (in the same way as a number line). History really is very difficult for a young child to comprehend — the years before their birth are history! A time-line may do little to alter this at primary level but at least they will have a framework to build on as their perception grows. For example, maybe when talking about homes in the past, the time-line could be alongside any display work.

SCIENCE

It is a good idea to set up a science bench or table and to keep changing the objects on it. Often science and experiments can easily be incorporated into a topic and then displays and experiments are straightforward. Occasionally science is left out of a topic so compensation for this must be made, e.g. putting lenses, microscopes and objects to look carefully at (other suggestions will be made at the end).

Collecting and classifying. A continuation of the 'sets' idea, but classification can be developed into more subtle groupings, e.g. 'Buildings topic' — classifying material as to waterproof, absorbency, flameproof, etc. Label work carefully.

Observation. Factual writing and drawings to begin to develop a *concise and accurate style of reporting observations.*

There are many other study skills which should be introduced (obviously basic skills continue to be taught at the same time).

Modelling and painting — recognition of scale.
Imaginative writing — personal and based on first-hand experiences.
Mathematics — graphs, shapes — to make some aspects of maths more meaningful to the child.
Questionnaires — simple yes–no answers (questioning each other). Use of tape recorder.
Comparisons — past with present.
Letter writing — e.g. thanking visitors.

An environmental topic should generally be spread over about half a term. In each case we should always begin with the child's personal experiences.

The links between various kinds of learning experience under a particular topic title are, in the preceding extract, much clearer and more explicit than we have seen in the much-favoured flow chart; and a document of this kind represents a useful attempt to marry rationale and systematic topic-planning in a form accessible to, and comprehensible by, even new or inexperienced staff in any given school setting.

Planning is now shared. Each teacher can see where his or her own class stands in relation to others. There are some underlying implications about progression through the scheme. All staff share some perceptions about their overall goals and philosophy. This discovery leads us on to explore the remaining questions listed above under the headings of intentions and planning procedures (p. 143).

These remaining questions deal with the length of time teachers take to prepare topics, whether they do so in any systematic way, whether and how they share their planning, and whether this planning is re-used and the topics repeated with other classes at a later date. Questions such as these were probed in the case studies by means of detailed questionnaires, used by caseworkers, and some flavour of the range of responses can be appreciated in the following extracts:

151

CSW. What planning and preparation do you do in order to tackle a new topic with a class? Let's concentrate on content and teaching methods first.

Teacher (of fourth-year junior class). The school has schemes of work in the three topic areas: history, geography and science. So when a teacher moves from one year group to another there is a scheme, in principle, to follow. The ability level of the class is an important aspect of planning the content. There are occasions when a topic arises which is not on the scheme for a particular year, but if there is enough interest the topic can be followed through.

CSW. What about preparing materials and resources that you need for a new topic?

Teacher. We have an extensive resources catalogue which contains a wealth of material. Some projects, of course, lend themselves better to modelling work, for example, than others. Here again, some projects 'take off' more than others and yet originally don't seem so interesting. The library service is excellent for short-term loans (which are ordered the term before). The museum service also; but this can be hit or miss for films or models. The children themselves bring many materials and resources to lessons.

CSW. How about preparing the classroom itself?

Teacher. Display space is needed for project work plus the posters which might accompany the project. Children don't observe in a classroom, though; the classroom display could be changed every week and quite a few wouldn't even notice. The pupils need to be taught to observe as well as listen. The only classroom preparation needed is to have one's materials ready for use.

CSW. How far ahead do you plan your topic work?

Teacher. It depends on the topic and the ability of the children: usually a week of two beforehand but if project collections are required, or a film, it's the term before.

This second extract shows a more systematic approach, but perhaps a less flexible one, with suburban seven to eight year olds:

In planning the content and teaching methods of a new topic:

1. *I meet with other year teachers to discuss the topic and the resources.*

2. *We list the things to be covered and make a flow chart.*

As for resources,

1. *I collect together a good range of books from the school library and County Lending Service. Children also bring and share their books from home.*
2. *I look up TV programmes which may fit, and get ready video recordings made in previous years.*
3. *I get ready my own materials and visual aids.*

For the classroom,

1. *I prepare a display area, e.g. pictures of the seashore and a collection of shells, etc.*
2. *I have an appropriate time-line ready, if this is required.*
3. *I put on display words to be used in the topic.*

We plan a whole term's topic at once in our year group, with flow chart and timetable; and several meetings and discussions are held to this end over about two weeks.

These two extracts give an impression of how the preparatory processes work before a topic is embarked upon. However, when a large number of these extracts are viewed side by side a much more detailed picture emerges, which is of more immediate value to a practitioner. The Topic-Work Project had access to over a hundred such statements about preparation from its case studies and from the earlier questionnaire phase of its research. The paragraphs that follow summarise this information in a form which may assist a practising teacher to adopt a methodology of his or her own.

PROCESSES FOR PREPARATION IN TOPIC WORK

Extensive questioning of teachers about how far in advance they prepared for a particular topic showed that somewhere between a month and half a term was a common period within which they thought about the approaching theme. Preparation was sometimes carried out in vacation times, sometimes during term-time. Our conjecture was that a typical project consumes about one working week in its gestation, either as a concentrated block of holiday-period time or in snatches during the term. A few teachers only gave preparation more time than this: though some schools clearly had forecasts of topic titles covering a whole academic year. In these cases activities such as resource collection proceeded almost continuously. Just a handful of teachers left planning until a day or so before the event, and where they did it was usually because they tied work strongly to a television series over which they had no personal control.

Planning was often shared between teachers. The commonest pattern was for staff in one year group to work together to outline a flow diagram, to share visits or resources, and to trade ideas.

Rarely did these co-operative planning exercises lead to co-operative classroom work, e.g. team-teaching.

Two-thirds of the teachers questioned did repeat topics from year to year with new classes when they felt it appropriate to do so. This strategy met with varied success. At one extreme:

The topic developed different approaches, and brought to light different ideas as well as similar ones. Emphasis and enthusiasm for themes had changed. The class discovered fresh material. Individualised pieces of work were widely different.

But sometimes the experiment failed: the teacher felt jaded or had failed to respond to the quite different interests of a new class.

Most teachers we interviewed or questioned had a fairly systematic approach to preparation. We noted patterns emerging in the teachers' responses to questions about preparation procedures. It was decided to distil these patterns into a checklist, which emerged as follows:

Teachers' reported preparations for topic work

Before the topic begins, in the areas of *content and teaching methods*, teachers

1. make flow diagrams or outlines of anticipated directions of study
2. divide the content into the curriculum areas to be covered
3. decide on specific teaching activities or modes for subdivision of the content
4. refer to the school's outline scheme of work
5. read around the subject at their own level
6. make a list of the skills to be taught

154

7. make notes on classroom management procedures (e.g. assign pupils to working groups)
8. decide on the time-scale of the topic
9. amend their flow chart or plans in consultation with pupils
10. plan lead lessons
11. subdivide the topic into progressive stages
12. decide on the format of desired outcomes
13. maintain a detailed record-book or notes
14. look at the TV programme guides
15. formulate aims and objectives
16. carry out pre-topic stimulus activities such as visits
17. think out suitable work for most and least able
18. find out how much the children already know
19. are sensitive to early responses and expressed interests of pupils
20. share out jobs between teachers in a team
21. provide pupils with Banda sheets of the scheme of work

In the areas of finding *resources and materials*, teachers

1. make a search of school and public libraries
2. collect suitable audio-visual software
3. arrange visits and speakers
4. contact museums and other outside organisations
5. prepare worksheets or assignment cards
6. encourage pupils, colleagues or parents to collect materials
7. consult TV and radio programme schedules
8. write letters to supplying agencies
9. visit the local Teachers' Centre
10. view in advance any area to be visited later by the class
11. collect natural items from the local environment
12. gather together any required equipment (like jars)
13. run off Banda sheets
14. check the budget
15. make word lists of key-words for the classroom walls

In *preparing the classroom* itself, teachers

1. make a display of related charts, reference books, etc.
2. prepare a display area
3. prepare resource collections
4. decide on the layout of furniture

155

5. check that any software or apparatus required is readily available
6. provide suitable folders on storage for pupils' work
7. organise outside or ancillary help
8. explore the potential of school-based facilities (such as rain-gauges)

This checklist has in its turn anticipated some of the questions about preparation raised initially in chapter 3, and has in effect answered some of the following with respect to teachers in our questionnaire and case-study samples:

Questions of resource and teaching method

In planning, do you look to resources and resource people beyond the school gates — the teachers' centre, potential speakers, places to visit, parents?

How do you decide upon the most appropriate teaching methods for any given topic? For each topic lesson?

Questions of classroom organisation

What account do you take of what pupils already know?

How do you find this out?

Is your classroom orderly?

Do pupils know where basic resources and pieces of equipment are?

Can they get on without fussing?

Do they have the requisite study skills — adequate reading ability, knowledge of an index, etc.?

If not, is study-skills acquisition built into the topic?

Have you thought ahead to provide suitable alternative activities for the slowest? The most able?

Is everything ready in advance?

The foregoing checklist has illustrated how and in what order teachers tend to tackle these problems. To what extent they are successful in so doing, and the strategies adopted by our case-studied teachers, can be more effectively explored in the next chapter, which deals with the processes of teaching. This leaves us with just two more sets of questions about preparation that can be explored from the case-study data; and to these we now turn our attention.

BUILDING IN THE MONITORING PROCESSES

Effective tracking of pupils' progress during a project means that some criteria for success need to be articulated before the work begins. Ideally, the intentions of a piece of topic work, spelled out at the preparation stage, delineate the kinds of learning which should take place and therefore imply the kinds of monitoring which the teacher should attempt during and after the work. Hence in chapter 3 we looked at:

> **Questions of pupils' learning**
>
> **Have you devised some way(s) of monitoring the extent to which children are acquiring**
>
> > **the items of knowledge**
> > **the practical and social skills**
> > **the concepts and ideas**
>
> **you regard as essential or desirable for learning through this topic?**
>
> **How are you carrying out this monitoring process?**
>
> **To whom, besides yourself, is the information relevant?**
>
> **How will it be imparted? When? For what purpose?**

Some responses to these questions were considered in the previous chapter on curriculum management. The management process may lay down some form of record-keeping as a prerequisite for all staff, and in some schools the record-keeping proforma is a well-developed document. Where such documents exist, their nature must inevitably help to form part of the teacher's planning strategy. But schools with such a fully thought-out approach to records for topic-work curriculum are in a minority, and a small minority at that. So the case studies set out to explore what other kinds of monitoring helped teachers in their planning strategies. The range proved enormous, and three extracts from cases serve to illustrate this judgement. The first is quite short:

CSW. How do you assess pupils' work in topic lessons?
Teacher (of a fourth-year class in an underprivileged middle school).
(a) By effort and (b) by achievement (e.g. general progress and
presentation of work). Effort and progress are easily recognised.
Achievement is measured by one's expectations of standards
attainable by the child.

A more detailed appraisal of desired learning outcomes is
provided by Jeannette, a teacher of second-year juniors at Dovecote
Mill primary — a school already described in some detail on pp. 89–
104. The caseworker reports:

Her class is engaged in the topic 'Water'. If all goes well it will last
for the whole of the spring term . . . Her expectations about what
the children will learn and how they will respond include:

> *knowledge of the properties of water*
> *uses of water*
> *dangers and problems caused by too much or too little water*
> *heightened awareness of water in the environment and its part in*
> *our lives.*

The topic also provided opportunities to practise skills which
Jeannette listed as:

comprehension
experimental
manipulative
note-making
recording
analysis of poems
creative prose writing
following verbal instructions
gleaning information from a text
picking out relevant information
organising information

A third extract, from a fourth-year junior teacher at Roseborough
primary, described in detail in chapter 2, describes how intentions,
teaching/learning processes and monitoring belong together as a
coherent whole:

Conversation with a teacher at Roseborough primary

CSW. The background to what goes on here is the book *All the years round*. Can I ask you to describe how this kind of work takes place on a day-to-day basis in the classroom?

PC. Within the school generally each teacher has a plan based on *All the years round* but adapted by the year-group leader. There is room for manoeuvre for the individual teacher, who can adapt this scheme according to individual interests and strengths. In my class the work is based on the fact that all the pupils are at different stages; so it's not knowledge but understanding that counts. As a basis for this we use the classification system. With this pupils handle materials; can quickly work at a sensory level; then move on to mathematical levels — weight, density; and the biological if the object is a plant, or a human level if the object is an artefact.

CSW. That's the general picture and it comes over very strongly in the classroom. Let me take up an earlier point. You mentioned the horizontal structure of year-group leaders, and this is evidenced in the school. How does it relate to a vertical structure?

PC. Within the scheme there are three components.

1. *The development of man.* This is an outline of man's progress but it is not historical. It's a way of ensuring each year group will know what has gone before and what is to come; there may be reinforcement but there isn't unnecessary repetition. This element begins with pupils' experience and works backwards. We don't begin with the Norman invader and progress to the German invader; we'd begin with the current Falklands invasion and apply insights to the past.

2. *The habitat approach.* Uniformly throughout the school pupils are thinking along the same lines. At the centre of their thoughts is the sun: source of energy. In year one it's an elementary concept of the sun giving heat and light; they feel heat and possibly record temperature. The concept deepens as they progress through the school, so that they become aware of its habitat connotations: air, water and earth combine to become the crucial building-blocks of the world. They do simple experiments with plants. By year four they will be thinking in concepts like precipitation, condensation, and deposition of minerals. These are related to the sun's energy;

> air cycle, water cycle, mineral cycle are all ideas which are worked over and deepened. And they always think of the needs of an animal in a habitat. In year one they look at their own basic needs: shelter, warmth, needs. But each year adds sophistication.
>
> 3. *The importance of understanding.* We regard understanding as the first priority; the development of skills needed to acquire knowledge is secondary; and then they acquire knowledge and may end up quite knowledgeable children *as well*.

CSW. You make this distinction between understanding and knowledge: this must emanate from an underlying philosophy. Can you articulate this?

PC. The best way to illustrate this is with an example. A slow pupil, Mark, in a first-year class was asked: have you a pet? He had a dog. He was asked: what kind of dog? And he replied: 'It's brown and it barks.' To him that was a concept of a dog: simple, real, emotional, sensory. As Mark has gone through the school he has learned that his pet is canine, carnivore, etc. These are words which he uses: and if you asked what a carnivore was he could talk about the dog's teeth. So the label covers a mass of ideas; and these labels and concepts are a common language within the class. Some pupils will understand them more deeply than others, but the language is shared.

CSW. The common-language idea was an idea the oldest pupils themselves talked about on tape when I asked them about their work. I asked them how they knew when to use technical, scientific language, e.g. 'deduce', and when to use poetic forms. They were clear that there were guidelines in the classroom and that these were gradually assimilated by being present in the class. But many people would challenge that this approach is not possible with young children (though it's used here with eight-year-olds). How would you counteract that challenge?

PC. Experiences of visits, visitors and materials inevitably develop the right levels of learning if the control is right. We stress 'deduction' as an important element of the scheme. For example, we show the pupils a frog and give them the word 'amphibian'. This is no more irrelevant than meaningless strings of spellings: for the object and source of the concept is in front of them so they can use (not necessarily spell) the language. Once I've given them the language with its conceptual ramification they can use it to

deduce. I might say: tell me all you can about Semoria. That's
a strange, irrelevant word, some would say. But, equipped with
language and concepts, the pupils can work out the chain.
Equipped with the key that Semoria is an extinct amphibian, they
can work out: amphibian is like frog; frog needs damp;
frog/tadpole; frog/spawn, etc. The concept recalls experiences.
So I ask: if Semoria is an amphibian what would its egg be like?
They would deduce: eggs like jelly, cold-blooded, hibernating,
young look like tadpoles, with gills, with tail at birth but no legs.
So it's a logical method of thinking and of presenting ideas.

CSW. Arising from this description, let's look at two more questions. I asked the pupils where they would use this new language
learned in the classroom. They told me that they might recount
school events to Mum, but they wouldn't use it elsewhere. Now
there are some people who see social subversion in all we do in
school. Are you cutting these pupils off from their environment?

PC. I don't think so. We have an obligation to extend a child's
language. Different forms of language serve different purposes;
but we are enriching their language and equipping them for a
more scientific world. Too often in the past one has had to wait
until one went to college to make *sense* of knowledge.

CSW. Well, then, if we accept the position on language, what do you
say to the charge that *All the years round* is over-systematic and
mechanistic?

PC. If anyone can show me an unstructured learning system that's
as effective I would be interested. Passage through school can be
wearying precisely because one is often unsure of where learning
is going. But even structured schemes are often too knowledge-
bound: they have little to do with experience, relevance,
understanding and individual capabilities. There's too much rote-
learning without sense. We try to produce the sense-structure for
problem-solving. The scheme itself is flexible; but the framework
of principles remains common across the school.

CSW. Let's go on to record-keeping and criteria for success in this
work. Can you describe how you keep track of progress and on
what criteria you make judgements about whether the progress is
satisfactory?

PC. Because there's structure, record-keeping and monitoring are a
simple process. One would take any child in the class and ask him
to go through the classification procedure. He may say: it's man-
made or natural. So one asks: why? At that point the nature of
the answer reveals whether he or she has grasped the conceptual

structure and how effective the teaching process has been. If the child can go on: it's natural, organic, animal, invertebrate, mollusc, bi-valve . . . then one begins to realise the child has a deep understanding about this range of animals. At each point, to check the conceptual level, one simply has to ask the question why? or for justification of the statement.

Similarly, when the pupils move from class to class individual pupil ratings are quick to make; one can see where they've got through the conceptual framework. Pupils here are not given a view of themselves as failures. When they put forward ideas, then ideas are soundly based because of this system. The idea may turn out to be factually incorrect; but the logic may be sound and sensible. We discourage one-word answers; we give them an environment or material. But we ensure they think through the categories of the systems — not 'weasel' but, 'it moves, eats, breathes, is animal, vertebrate, mammal, stoat-like, no black tip to tail . . . therefore probably weasel'. So the child is not just wrong; he picks up positive responses from teachers and classmates . . .

Only the third of these extracts pursues the question of the value of the records and information which result from monitoring topic work. In the third example not only do intentions, processes and outcomes have a coherence, but staff are aware of this coherence and can 'plug into' it at any point to learn more about the pupils and their capabilities. It has to be said that such careful assessment procedures were rare; and this theme will be taken up again in detail in the next chapter but one.

SUMMARY

Thus it is that we might do well to pause in our review of preparation issues to see what has been learned from the cases extracted and discussed.

To date we have looked at the extent to which topics are planned and to what degree they evolve. We have seen how the construction of a flow diagram constitutes a basic planning strategy by teachers; but we have noted that these flow charts reveal typologies. The typologies themselves suggest underlying philosophies of education. We have pursued other planning strategies which seem to be stretching towards a more holistic view of curriculum; and we have noted the extent and duration of teachers' planning for topic work. From a wide range of cases and completed questionnaires we have compiled a checklist of planning operations. Latterly, we have explored the relationship between the planning process and the need to monitor what children learn.

We have neglected one question or issue under this planning theme, perhaps the most important question of all. It is to this that we turn our attention finally in this chapter.

A question of criteria

What criteria help you to formulate the choice of a specific topic?

Before preparation can begin, the teacher must decide specifically what topic he or she is going to cover. The question enlarges itself also into one of topic sequences: which topic first? which next? which ones to cover a primary-school career? The issues were raised by the Roseborough extract most recently quoted.

So how exactly is this choice made and what criteria determine the selection?

One criterion certainly informs the choice of many teachers: that of pupils' expressed interests. The point is made in this extract of sentences from a case study more fully reported on pages 133–142.

The children then posed the questions and the teachers directed them to a certain amount of research necessary . . . they were then able to work out for themselves . . . Unlike the questions that are set in their textbooks . . . the problems developed . . . through the children's own experiences . . .

Some other criteria are widespread but implicit and, almost without exception, have to be deduced. They are:

1. That the topic should impart knowledge about the world around us, i.e. should begin where the child is and in the environment;

2. That the topic should include and exemplify the working of certain discrete disciplines, often those of history, geography and science, though others might be included as well;

3. That through these disciplinary perspectives brought to bear

163

on a theme will emerge a certain level of knowledge, skill or concept acquisition appropriate to the age and ability of the child.

Thus the criteria are not articulated, but they are seen at work, as the following extract from a staff handbook shows. It begins with a description of why the handbook was compiled and goes on to break down a topic, 'Building', as an example.

Extract from staff handbook, Blaydon CP School

THE GUIDELINES

The HMI survey of Primary Education pointed to three areas, science, geography and history, where it was felt schools often lacked a clear policy. The topics chosen in this syllabus were carefully structured so as to avoid repetition of work in successive years, to maintain a progression and to avoid large areas of neglect in knowledge, experiences and skill development.

However, as a result of a working party in environmental studies by teachers in 1979, a framework of guidelines evolved which did not constitute a syllabus but rather an aid to the teacher's thinking when planning a topic and a yardstick against which the progress of the children may be measured.

These guidelines were divided into eight sections.

1. *Land-forms, solid and minerals*	
2. *The locality and beyond*	**GEOGRAPHY**
3. *The earth and its atmosphere*	
4. *People and occupations*	
5. *Economics and trade*	**HISTORY**
6. *Energy and power*	
7. *Water*	**SCIENCE**
8. *Plants and animals*	

SECOND-YEAR BUILDING TOPIC

Starting point: A new house or a building site close to school.

Skills   *Examples of activities*

Observations: Stages in building a house.
Discussions: The site: part of street, housing estate.

Nature of the ground, aspect, position of the sun, shadows — use of compass.

Planning the house: work of the surveyor, architect, builder — surveyor's instruments — chain, metre-stick, tape, spirit-level, theodolite, plumb-bob. Ground plans, elevations, blueprints.

Levelling the ground: digging the foundations, trenches, men at work, machines and tools used.

What is it like under the ground?

1. Soil, subsoil, rock.
2. Where else can we discover what it is like underground? (quarries, mines, pot-holes, caves)

Building materials: What will be needed?

1. Things needed for foundations, walls, roof, windows, doors, etc. Where materials come from.
2. Manufacture of bricks, cement, wood, iron, glass, etc. Transport of materials.
3. Concrete mixer — how it works. How bricks are laid. The tools used.

Services:
Water supply, drains, lighting, heating and cooking.

House into a home:

1. Give it a number or a name.
2. Moving in and making friends.

Science 1. Make a list of materials used in building and collect samples for observation and experiment.

2. Why were these particular materials used in certain places?

(a) *Put materials in water and see if they rust or rot.*

(b) *See if they take in water (children may be led to suggest that they weigh the object before and after).*

(c) *See if it lets water through. Compare with plastic sheet, leather (an old shoe), cloth.*

3. How strong is the material? (Load strips of material with weights — stones or bricks.)
4. Use of pulleys on buildings. Make simple pulleys with cotton reels. Try lifting with several small pulleys.
5. Use of wheels and rollers.
6. Painting — painted and unpainted iron in water.

Classification	*Categories of houses — detached, terraced, bungalow. Building materials — wood, metal, brick. Furnishing materials — wood, textiles.*
Factual writing	*1. 'How we tested the brick': writing about scientific experiments.* *2. Material from reference books.*
Reference books	*Where applicable in the topic at the appropriate level — see earlier first-year notes.*
Creative writing	*Through first-hand experiences on the building site, at Tattershall Castle, etc.*
Questionnaire and interviews	*Simple list of questions:* *Where do you live? What type of house do you live in? Simple Yes/No questions. Children question each other on basis of questionnaire. Introduction of tape recorder for interviews.*
Mathematics	*Plans, measuring, shape of articles, graphs, simple co-ordinate grids of rooms.*
Mapping	*Plans of rooms, houses and school (not to scale).*

166

Compass points. Large maps of locality. Designing room arrangements. Show where building materials come from on wall maps.

Use of time-line	1. *The ordinary home — a class book of the development of houses, or frieze from caves to high-rise blocks.* 2. *Defensive buildings — development of the castle (after visit to Tattershall Castle).*
Drawing	*My house, machines on the building site.*
Modelling	*Local houses, houses of the past, castles.*
Display	*'Street diorama', frieze of house types. Group books.*

So it appears that there is a working philosophy which informs the choice of topic titles in the primary sector. But, with the possible exception of Roseborough school, none of our studied schools argued for particular content or for a minimum skill or concept mastery consisting of specified components which all pupils should have acquired or experienced by the age of transfer to secondary education. It is an issue which must be held in abeyance at this juncture, to be pursued again in the closing chapter of the book.

6

Classroom Processes:
1. The Teaching Context

I remember once watching a film about a young schoolmaster. The message of the film was that, little by little, the abrasive incidents of classroom contact wore down this inexperienced but well-intentioned young man. Finally, after a long process of attrition, he was drowned by his pupils during a school journey to the seaside. Whether his fate was real or allegorical was a question the viewer was left to decide for himself. Either way, the film pointed out two important facets of classroom life — that it consists of a series of usually fleeting inter-personal contacts and that it is in the quality of these contacts that the success or failure of the teacher resides.

This chapter and the next set out to explore what happens in classrooms, the processes of teaching. We begin by asking a quite fundamental question.

WHAT DO TEACHERS DO DURING TOPIC LESSONS?

It is easy to take for granted the more obvious aspects of one's profession. Plainly, teachers teach; and we each have a concept in our mind of what that verb means. However, if each of us were to verbalise that concept it is quite likely that we would not just disagree about detail (whether the teacher uses a blackboard or an overhead projector to reinforce a point), but *or* probably over quite central issues (whether teaching more nearly implies a description of a talk to the whole class or a drama session in which the teacher acts as a spectator of pupils' plays). These important variations in how the description 'teaching' could be used led us in our case studies of topic work to ask a question at a more basic level: what do teachers actually *do* during topic lessons?

In order to explore this question a method was devised to look systematically at what teachers were doing during a segment of each lesson that was case-studied. The following description of the method of working and of analysing the observations will clarify the process.

During a segment of each studied lesson lasting approximately fifteen minutes the caseworker wrote down at thirty-second intervals what the teacher was doing at that moment, thus:

30 seconds: *Prompts Robert for an answer.*
1 minute: *Gives information.*
1.30:   *Asks question.*
2 minutes: *Explains 'environmental health'.*

At the end of 15 minutes the caseworker had thus generated thirty tallies: and each one was in the form of a description containing a verb describing the activity. These verbs were key-words in analysing the data, for many recurred (e.g. questions, explains, informs, listens). Using these key-words it was possible to devise a series of broad categories which described teachers' activities: administering, monitoring, talking and listening. Each category could be subdivided; for example, in the case of 'monitoring' it was found to be possible to record whether the target in each instance was the class, a group of pupils or an individual.

The results of this study of teachers' activities are displayed in Table 6.1. The table shows the results of a study (Miles 1983) of two teachers in a large primary school located in a busy market town. Freehand description of the teachers' styles, and their responses in interviews with the caseworker, had suggested that these two teachers had rather different approaches to their task. Some dimensions of these approaches can probably be explored through the systematic data collected in Table 6.1. The case-study worker observed two teachers systematically during a series of topic lessons. In each case the teachers' activities were analysed and coded. Table 6.1 sets out the results, which are instructive.

The first discovery is that both teachers talked a lot of the time (52 per cent and 61.6 per cent of activities respectively); and clearly one has here, potentially, some measure of the verbal dominance of the teacher over the lesson. For teacher A, explaining occupied only one-fifth of these talking acts (10.9 per cent of all recorded activities), while for teacher B explaining (at 26 per cent of all recorded activities) was more central to his whole approach to his

Table 6.1: The teachers' activities during project lessons

Teachers' activities	Teacher A		Teacher B	
	No. of acts	% of total	No. of acts	% of total
Administering				
1. Taking the register	3	1.6		
2. Taking bookshop money	5	2.6		
3. Preparing for lesson	7	3.6		
4. Writing on blackboard			4	1.7
5. Organising children	19	9.8	5	2.1
6. Giving out equipment	7	3.6	11	4.7
7. Fetching equipment for:				
self	1	0.5	10	4.3
child	3	1.6		
8. Discipline	15	7.8	6	2.6
9. Interruption	2	1.0	6	2.6
	62	32.1	42	18.0
Monitoring				
1. Class	9	4.7	7	3.0
2. Group	3	1.5		
3. Individual	5	2.6	2	0.8
	17	8.8	9	3.8
Talking				
1. Explaining	21	10.9	61	26.0
2. Questioning	39	20.2	52	22.1
3. Answering	3	1.5	1	0.4
4. Recalling previous work	5	3.0	13	5.5
5. Setting task	2	1.0	3	1.3
6. Reading	8	4.1	3	1.3
7. Discussing with:				
class	2	1.0	5	2.1
group	15	7.8		
individual	3	1.5	2	0.8
8. Prompting children to answer	2	1.0	2	0.8
9. Indulging in humour/jokes			3	1.3
	100	52.0	145	61.6

Table 6.1: contd.

Teachers' activities	Teacher A		Teacher B	
	No. of acts	% of total	No. of acts	% of total
Listening				
1. Answering	7	3.6	26	11.1
2. Discussing	1	0.5	1	0.4
3. Questioning	3	1.5	1	0.4
4. Reading	3	1.5	11	4.7
	14	7.1	39	16.6
Total	193	100.0	235	100.0

Note

Administering:
3 — moving chairs and tables, looking at notes, discussion with another teacher.
5 — moving children, what the children need from drawers.
9 — head teacher, secretary, hail outside, door blew open.

Talking:
1 — a word, what they are going to do, new knowledge, relating own experiences, describing things, using display and demonstrations, why examples of children's work are so good.
2 — all levels, either to class, group or individual discipline.
7 — discussion on new knowledge, interesting point out of explanation, or something said, involves both teacher's and pupils' participation.

Source: A. Miles, 'Developing pupils' thinking through topic work: a personally conducted case-study', BEd dissertation (University of Nottingham, 1983).

topic lessons. Both teachers made quite extensive use of questions (a more detailed analysis of these questions appears later in the chapter).

Though he talked a lot, teacher B was also a relatively frequent listener, especially to what children had to say in answer to his questions (16.6 per cent of all activities tallies, as opposed to teacher A's 7.1 per cent). Because of his class-based teaching style, teacher B did less monitoring than teacher A.

This table, though relatively crude, is in fact giving us clues about quite sophisticated concepts of teaching such as 'style'; in other words about the relative frequency of certain teaching behaviours and their implications for the ways in which children are encouraged to learn. It is highlighting questions about the context of these classroom processes — whether this is the whole-class teaching mode, a group context or one of individualised learning. These issues must be examined in due course, though first we can complete this bird's-eye view of teachers A and B afforded by the table itself.

The strongest contrast between the two teachers, and the most significant one perhaps, is in the area of activity concerned with administration. None of the administration categories is about learning; each is concerned with the context in which learning may potentially operate or is about the management chores that beset the teacher. Teacher A spends almost one-third of her teaching activities on one or other administrative task, while teacher B has reduced this figure to below a fifth (32.1 per cent and 18 per cent respectively).

Some further implications of these figures in Table 6.1 are drawn out in the paragraph which follows and then pursued in depth throughout this chapter.

In chapter 3 we examined in outline those issues and questions relating to the broad theme of classroom processes. The findings in Table 6.1 suggest that these sets of issues can now be explored more carefully. First in this chapter, the issue relating to management skills requisite in the teacher is pertinent in the light of our discoveries about teachers' involvement in various kinds of administrative tasks. Secondly, we can proceed to examine more critically the classroom context for topic teaching by looking at teaching modes. Thirdly, we can move on to examine specific teaching skills such as questioning and task-setting; and a discussion of these skills will follow in chapter 7.

CLASSROOM ORGANISATION

So we turn to management matters, and ask:

A question of organisation and management

What organisation and management skills do teachers need to tackle topic work effectively?

To some extent this question might be answered by examining the list of 'administering' activities in Table 6.1, namely,

taking the register
taking the money
preparing furniture
writing on the blackboard
organising children
giving out equipment
fetching equipment
keeping discipline
coping with interruptions

What is immediately apparent, however, is that the real skills here lie in the ability to eliminate, as far as possible, the intrusions of these events into classroom learning. Taking the register is streamlined if the teacher simply spots and checks on absentees rather than roll-calling. Furniture can often be placed appropriately in *advance* of the lesson. Giving out books and equipment can likewise be done in advance or delegated to sensible pupils. In a well-run school classroom interruptions will be minimal, and the procession of 'pupils on errands' which features in some schools is simply unprofessional since it disrupts teaching.

Table 6.1 has simple mathematical implications for topic (or any other) teaching: the greater the proportion of activities devoted to managing the fewer remain for learning.

But Table 6.1 does not exhaust the skills of organisation and management needed by teachers. Two important areas of skill are in preparation for lessons and in administrative planning. By the latter, what is meant is those activities that take place beyond the classroom: arranging field work, contacting visiting speakers, writing letters and making telephone calls. Teachers receive little training in these fields and, though they might be expected to be intelligent enough to perform these functions efficiently, this is not always the case. It is worth suggesting in passing that some in-service training might profitably be devoted to these teacher functions; but it is no part of the present brief to pursue the matter. By contrast, preparation processes are discussed in greater detail in chapter 5; and are not discussed again here since it is assumed that these will have been completed before the lesson begins. Here the focus of attention is on the lesson itself; and so we can move on to look at questions about the context in which learning takes place.

THE CONTEXT OF LEARNING

Here we set out to examine

Questions about teaching mode

How can the three main teaching modes best be employed for topic teaching?

What are the most suitable uses for whole-class work?

What is the function of group work?

How can pupils be assigned to these groups?

Should the criteria for group assignment change from time to time? When? How? Why?

Is individualised learning used? When? How?

Are the pupils really equipped to work independently?

Have they the necessary study skills?

Can they make decisions for themselves?

Are they able to determine, in part, the directions in which their own work should travel? When they should move on?

Most topic work observed by the caseworkers in our study contained a blend of whole-class teaching and group work; sometimes individualised learning[1] replaced group work, or was a way of working with some pupils (the bright, the slow, and those with specific needs and interests). Our questionnaire to participant teachers asked the respondents to describe the part played by each mode; and, while one cannot talk of a 'typical' response since each was unique, this one contains recurrent features:

Whole-class teaching is used to introduce topics, and to teach some study skills such as map work. I begin and end lessons by calling the class together, to discuss the work in progress.

For about half of our allotted topic time the children work in groups. Sometimes these groups represent a mix of ability, sometimes the pupils are deliberately put into 'sets'. Group tasks are often rather formal, i.e. the group aim is very specific and the role of each child is spelled out.

Following upon whole-class work or group tasks the able children are often anxious to move on much more rapidly, and this is where individuals can work appropriately.

(A fourth-year teacher and deputy head in a large, modern split-site suburban school with a diverse catchment area and offering conventional but cramped conditions.)

The quotation raises some issues that were widespread, and it is as well to list these and deal with them one by one. They are as follows:

1. The purposes and functions of whole-class work are often more clearly defined than those of individual work.
2. The 'mix' of pupils within groups is a matter of concern for teachers.
3. There is an important connection between the teacher's solution to the issues of 'mix' in the groups and the kinds of task that groups are seen to be able to tackle.
4. Teachers are less severe about defining and using the terms 'individual' and 'individualised', and in using genuinely individualised learning, than they are about employing the other two teaching modes.

Under these four areas we can take a closer look at classroom practice.

Purposes and functions of whole-class teaching

The project's questionnaire survey asked of a sample of 130 heads and teachers an identical question to that of the case-study interviews about the role of whole-class teaching. From the freehand responses received it was possible to identify clear purposes for whole-class teaching and to place these in rank order according to how frequently they were mentioned. The result of this analysis produces the following list:

To start off the topic, set the scene, assign jobs
To make sure relevant facts and information are shared
To allow for discussion
For summing up, revising, testing and following up
To allow progress reports and share findings of general interest
To add a stimulus to work in progress
For story, music, drama or oral activities

To alter the course of work in progress
To direct lines of enquiry
To start each lesson
For pupils to report to the class

Our case-studied teachers largely reflected these views about whole-class teaching, and some of the lesson accounts quoted in this book illustrate the point (see pp. 10–11).

Assigning pupils to groups

There can be little doubt that this decade has been the decade of the mixed-ability class at all levels of schooling from the infant department to the 'open-door' sixth form. In practice this means that the vast majority of primary teachers — our own small-scale surveys suggested almost 90 per cent — find themselves facing a class with a wide mix of ability. In a typical class of top juniors there may be six years' difference between the reading ages of the ablest and the least able readers; and other abilities will be similarly disparate. For this reason, and because the whole philosophy of the mixed-ability class seems to run counter to grouping by ability, teachers are often at a loss to know how to assign pupils to working groups. The relatively stable 'friendship pair' tends to have a majority vote: children sit and work with what some American researchers have called 'the most preferred co-worker'. Alternatives to this pairing are so-called 'hidden streams', or a deliberate mix of abilities into a group whose task is then subdivided so that each individual element is assigned to the pupil most suited to its particular level of demand. This last is altogether subtler; though it is doubtful whether its deviousness fools the pupils!

This then was the way in which most teachers in the case studies thought about assigning pupils to groups and these were the decisions to which they came about grouping criteria. It was rare for teachers to pursue the issue much further; though it is an important one because it determines the nature of tasks that can be set (see *Setting group tasks* below). One exception to these generalisations was Mrs Byrd, whose lessons with eight-year-olds in an EPA school are described in detail in chapter 2. Here is part of a conversation that reveals her thinking:

CSW. You mentioned slow learners; were the three pupils on this table here among the slow ones?

Mrs Byrd. No. The two girls are average. Johnny is below average. But both of the girls want to be leader. There *were* things going wrong at that table — but they were social. My philosophy is that social education *is* education. You have to learn from one another. I'm interested in learning, not information. But I shall intervene here and say: 'Why did that piece of learning not take place?' 'Why did you quarrel rather than stay on-task?' You might think they're a bit young for this; but I don't. They have to explore their own personalities and how groups work.

CSW. I noticed last week that in one group a little lad said: 'Look, we're getting side-tracked; this isn't part of the question.'

Mrs Byrd. Yes. It's important — a part of learning, being open to each other.

CSW. Many adults don't have this kind of chairmanship skill . . . But how do you group the pupils?

Mrs Byrd. Rarely by ability. Usually by shared interest. Often they rotate to a specific activity. Usually the groups are social. I believe people work better in self-chosen groups with just enough creative tension to spark each other off.

Here, then, is a distinctive view; and the concept of creative tension at least recalls us to the need to look at the implications of group constituency for task-setting and vice versa.

Setting group tasks

This section deals only with the specific problem which the teacher has in devising group tasks for a collection of pupils of widely different abilities; the more general issue of task-setting as a teaching skill is reserved for a later chapter. According to the respondents to the project's Phase One Questionnaire, groups were used:

  to complete a collective product: displays, collage, models, etc.
  to facilitate 'research' and information-gathering
  to give pupils a forum in which to solve problems
  to permit practical activities
  to enable pupils with similar interests to work together
  to encourage discussion

to carry out field work, visits and experiments
to do follow-up to whole-class inputs
to complete art work or drama
to practise group presentation of materials
to allow pupils to motivate one another
to encourage pupil–pupil interaction
for creative work and story writing
to carry out work in science
to perform tasks from work-cards
to carry out several different tasks at once
to provide opportunities for pupils to be leaders
to complete written work
to allow pupils to view and analyse each other's work
to stimulate the more able (in ability groups)
to permit the completion of group tasks

As with whole-class teaching, teachers were fairly clear about the kinds of work assigned to groups, though group work was not universal and the label was often used for pupils sitting together but working separately. Wide ranges of ability within the groups probably accounted for any limits to, or reservations about, its use.

Individual and individualised learning

Children of widely differing abilities taught as a class are offered an identical diet; and inevitably this cannot be suitable for each individual. In a class situation some will be bored while others struggle to keep up. The use of groups opens up a possible alternative in which pupils can work on tasks designed to fit their needs more closely while retaining a social context. But we have seen that these groups, too, often fail to solve the teacher's problems; and one could perhaps hypothesise that an ideal solution would be to blend whole-class work with activities in groups and with individualised work in which youngsters pursue topic interests at their own level and pace.

This kind of individualised learning has several prerequisites. First, pupils have to be equipped with the kind of study skills that make them functional: they must be able to locate information by using a library, a catalogue, an index and so on. They must be able to read fluently, to extract significant information, to précis and to re-order the data. Subsequently, these pupils will need to be acclimatised to working in an atmosphere where they are less teacher-dependent, where they can make decisions about when to proceed to the next step, and about the direction of travel. What evidence was there to suggest that our studied teachers used individualised learning; and how did they use it? A good place to begin to answer this question is at the infant level. In this extract we listen to a part-time teacher working in the infant class of a small rural primary school:

With the less able I try to give them individual help; I help them and talk to them about what we've done and what we've seen, about what we are writing, and sometimes I even write work for them to copy.

Another method I've used is to write a list of questions and ideas, and put these on card. I did this with the brighter ones last term — a sort of work-card. Then, if a pupil finished the topic work earlier than the rest, he or she could go on and work through a card of questions connected with what we had been doing. I would also expect a higher standard of work from the able individuals.

In the fourth year of the same school a similar methodology is adopted:

Most of the teaching has to be done on an individual basis (because of the wide spread of abilities in the class of 24 pupils). I might start a class lesson with everyone together, but a large part of my time is to go round and sort the children out as they're working because they've all got their own problems . . . I use work-cards, and that's mainly a reminder to me of what I'm doing with the class and also as extra work for the more able . . . When I first started using this system I stuck to the cards very rigidly, but I found out that it was a waste of time because some of the children couldn't read them. So sometimes I produce Banda sheets for those children to simplify the tasks, and I find that is the best way to do it . . . But I don't think children get a lot of choice over the tasks they do, though the more able are allowed a greater choice as to what they do after they've completed the set work for the lesson.

Thus individualised learning can still be teacher-dominated; and when pupils work alone it is usually more a case of individual work rather than individualised work — a state of play summed up in this brief quotation: 'I use this method particularly when I want the children to find out things from reference books.'

Nevertheless, there were some systematic attempts to give pupils study skills in order to allow them a measure of independence.

Extract from staff handbook, Blaydon CP School

ENVIRONMENTAL STUDIES SYLLABUS

Environmental Studies is based upon children learning through direct involvement in the study of their habitats.

It is intended as a means of helping children to develop a wide variety of skills for observing, recording and interpreting their world.

Nowadays, information is directed at children through television, radio, books and comics, on a scale never before achieved. From an early age children can see far-distant parts of the earth, the surface of the moon and Mars, remains of past peoples, and the wonders of science. Children faced with this mass of material need to develop, before reaching secondary stage, a wide range of methods of dealing with it.

Basically then our aims and objectives are to develop confident, enquiring children, aware of the nature, variety and beauty in the world, and having the skills to communicate their awareness in a variety of ways.

The skills needed to achieve these aims are in three main groups:

1. *The study skills (mapping, collecting and classifying of materials, experimenting, preparing interviews and questionnaires, using reference books, etc.).*
2. *The basic skills of language and mathematics.*
3. *Social skills — working in groups, attitudes to people, respect for the quality of their environment.*

With each year we hope to develop all skills along progressive lines. Careful grading of progress is not possible in the same ways as in reading and mathematics, but there must be progression in the learning of study skills and social skills as well as in basic skills.

SUMMARY

In this truncated review of the questions surrounding the issue of teaching mode we have seen a variety of practice by teachers, with all three modes used but usually in combination and with whole-class work quite dominant — more so, perhaps, than teachers are aware. The point is made in the transcript which is included in the next chapter. Thus we have examined the context of teaching and have reviewed some of the managerial skills required for a teacher to function effectively during lessons. We turn from these to the teaching skills which a teacher needs for effective topic work.

NOTE

1. A situation in which the teacher began a lesson with a short talk and then set children each to work on a single identical task is here called 'individual work'. Individualised learning implies that a given task is specifically devised to meet the needs of one specific pupil. Individualised learning may operate across all pupils in a class, or where other youngsters are engaged in group work.

7

Classroom Processes:
2. Teaching Skills and Professional Development

A LESSON OBSERVED

In this second chapter about classroom processes we turn our attention to the teaching skills which a teacher needs to tackle a topic-work lesson. The contention of this chapter is that these are many and various; and the methodology for examining them critically is therefore quite complicated. Thus we shall adopt a step-by-step approach, and the chapter begins by quoting in full a caseworker's account of a lesson in progress with a class of fourth-year pupils in a middle school. The reader should begin by working through this account so as to become familiar with it. As he reads he should bear in mind the questions about teaching skills highlighted in chapter 3:

Questions about teaching skills

What teaching skills are required of teachers in topic lessons?

How can these skills be refined and improved?

How can lessons be given variety in order to encourage pupils' enthusiasm and curiosity?

How does flexible teaching of the kind implied here affect demands on the general organisation and management skills of the teacher?

The theme of the tasks is 'Great Britain'. The teacher has provided a list of areas which relate to this theme (British inventors, famous people, kings and queens, historical events, geographical regions). Pupils are free to choose subjects from this list. They read about the subject, write notes and then make a fair copy of the information discovered in a special topic folder.

Case-study extract: Moore Cove School

Mr Prince: 3rd lesson observed; 11-year-olds

GREAT BRITAIN

1.12 p.m. The teacher is talking to the headmaster. The pupils are all seated, well behaved and working alone, though he is not present.

1.14 p.m. Teacher arrives and registers the class. Work continues.

1.16 p.m. A pupil, spontaneously, consults the teacher about a drawing of an Austin 7 and they exchange two sentences about it.

The teacher talks to the ancillary worker about ordering equipment.

Two pupils consult the teacher about equipment.

The teacher is sitting at his desk and is engaged upon his own chores. A group of three boys whisper occasionally; otherwise there is high task-involvement. Tasks in progress are:

1. Written work in topic-work folders.
2. Consulting reference books.
3. Drawing in topic folders.
4. Decorating margins.

I notice that most of the display board in the room is now covered with pupils' work and posters. (In retrospect I wonder what, if any, of this was for my benefit.)

1.25 p.m. The teacher moves off to monitor individual pupils at work.

T. What's wrong with this? (Nil response from pupil)

T. It's not the drawing, what's wrong with it? (Nil)

T. (Takes the pupil's work, goes to board, draws, asks class) A nice drawing, but what's wrong with it?

P2. The arrows aren't straight.

T. Right. (Takes work back to individual pupil.)

1.28 p.m. (Teacher moves on to monitor pupil 3; then pupil 4. Tells pupil not to neglect the margin decorations. Ancillary brings equipment. Teacher jokes with pupil. Looks at file again — checks incorrect capital letter. Moves on to pupil 5.)

T. That's a complicated border [i.e. margin design], isn't it? (A brief conversation ensues.)

T. (Checks chattering pupil.)

T. (to pupil 6) How about a title? (A pupil initiates a query about her work. The teacher tells the girl not just to make a list of inventors but to find out what they have invented.)

T. Have you looked through a list?

P. Yes.

T. Are there any names you recognise?

P. Faraday.

T. Find out about him. (Checks pupils for omitting titles on written work.)

T. Is that Concorde?

P. Yes.

T. Has anyone else written about Concorde? (Nil response)

T. Why Concorde? What's important about it?

P. It was the first passenger plane to travel that fast.

T. Yes — more than that.

P. It is supersonic.

T. Yes — the only and the first such plane. It may disappear for economic reasons. When you grow up, though, there will be a whole new generation of this kind of plane. On it, you don't just pay for a ticket but for the whole service . . . Is there anything in the reference books on Concorde or supersonic aircraft? (Teacher moves on. Turns to pupil 7.)

T. Have you looked at that list yet?

1.38 p.m. (Teacher breaks off to talk to a colleague.)

1.39 p.m. (Pupil initiates a contact — inaudible.)

1.40 p.m. (Teacher checks another pupil for chattering. Pupil 10 initiates an enquiry about the drawing of a physical map.)

T. What's going to be the main colour?

P. Yellow.

T. No — what kind of country is it?

P. High.

T. Look at an atlas for the information you need. (Moves on to next pupil: 11).

T. Who are you going to write about?

P. Don't know yet. (Teacher returns to his desk and looks at another pupil's work.)

T. You've got some good pieces of history and geography but nothing about famous men and women. Have a look . . . (various *suggestions. Then the teacher breaks off to talk to another pupil, but resumes; talking about what is important in a biography, i.e. a man's achievements. There follow one or two more brief monitoring interchanges.)*

WHOLE CLASS

1.45 p.m. T. Stop. Look at the board. Two things have come up today. One person has been writing a *list* of inventors. What's more important is their achievements and their importance for the world. So — look at the list of inventors I've given you; find a name you recognise. Faraday, for example. What do you know about Faraday?

P. Power?

T. Right. So this is important. Better than a list. Find a name of your own. Bring the name to me and I'll vet if he's important enough. Now looking at Christine's I see lots about kings and queens; little about science, farming, technology, industry. What was the subject we studied before?

P. The Industrial Revolution.

T. Right. So we know it's important. And a person we learned about who was head and shoulders above the world — a scientist — who was he? *(Three wrong responses.)*

P. Newton.

T. Yes; and I explained about his telescope. What was more important still about him?

P. Gravity.

T. Right.

P. It says here someone else invented the telescope.

T. Yes — but Newton's was best for the purpose. But what about this gravity thing?

P. It's a force pulling things down to earth.

T. If you had a long string and a weight; and if you held them side by side thus:

Figure 7.1

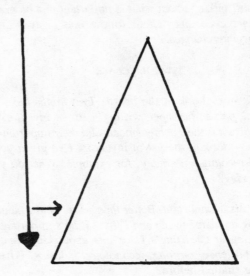

the weight would move in, towards the mountain — because of gravity.

P. It holds you down.

T. What do we call this — not a 'pull'?

P. Force.

T. *Good.* (Draws on board.) Suppose we climbed the highest building in the world and dropped a cannon ball and a marble simultaneously, in what order would they hit the pavement?

P. The bigger one, 'cos it's heavier.

T. Who disagrees?

P. (Several put up hands.)

T. Give me another solution.

P. Both at the same time.

T. Who thinks that? I used to find it difficult to believe. If you were on the moon and dropped a feather and a piece of metal simultaneously they would land at the same moment. The astronauts did it on TV. So was Newton right?

P. Yes.

T. I wish we had it on video. Now Newton said it but couldn't prove it. He said that the earth went round the sun by means of the gravity of the sun. We have a planet whizzing round us — the moon — held the same way. The Americans have made great use *of this knowledge in space research. (Draws on board).*

Figure 7.2

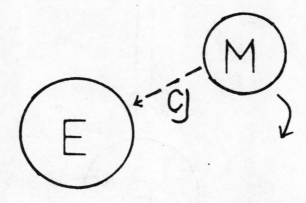

Now, the further away you get from earth the less pull is needed from the engines because gravity decreases. How did the spacemen demonstrate this lessening pull?

P. They floated around in the ship.

T. Yes. And they can switch off their engines. As they get nearer the sun, what will happen?

P. They'll speed up.

T. Yes; so when they're *descending*, what do they have to do?

P. Turn on motors.

T. What sort?

P. Retro-rockets.

T. What does that mean?

P. (explains)

T. Look at another application:

Figure 7.3

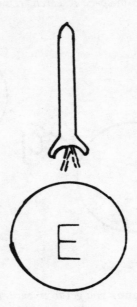

How does the vehicle change direction?
P. (incorrect response)
T. No. Look, they do it like this:

Figure 7.4

The Voyager 1 and 2 missions were like this. All this is based on gravity. Gravity can work against our interests or we can use it. What would happen if this craft went too slowly?

P. They'd get pulled down on to earth and crash.

T. Correct. If John shot a cannon like this

Figure 7.5

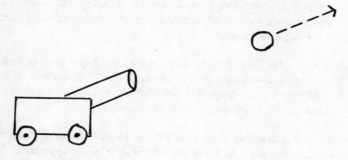

what would happen?

P. The dotted path should bend.

T. Yes — it'll curve:

Figure 7.6

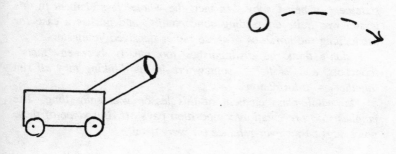

P. That's like the satellite orbit.

T. Yes. What happens if a satellite slows down?

P. It falls back to earth.

T. Has this happened?

P. (describes an incident — doesn't know which craft)

T. Suppose you were to switch on engines from earth and accelerate it?

P. It would go away from orbit and escape from the atmosphere.

T. Not from the atmosphere — from gravity. We know all this because of Newton. So it may be a good idea to find out something about him: not what he had for breakfast.

2.10 p.m. (Class reverts to working individually on topic-work folders. Teacher goes to desk. Monitors two pupils' work. Talks about where to find reference material. Interruption for netball team to go to a match.)

2.15 p.m. (Teacher checks on the work of a pupil who is looking not very enthusiastically at a reference book. He banters with the departing netball team. He helps an individual to find reference material. The bell goes. Orderly dismissal.)

After the lesson Mr Prince stops me to talk about his teaching strategies. He says he's not interested in a skills approach. He's more concerned that these pupils need to work on, and know, information. He's also concerned with good presentation, methods of composing, etc.

Reflections on the lesson (post-event)

I think Mr Prince has realised that his own approach and mine may be different in emphasis — he's a bit defensive about that, hence the statement of belief above. In fact, the whole-class element in this lesson was quite demanding conceptually; and he has a case for broadening the horizons of these rather deprived youngsters.

I don't think he distinguishes too clearly between 'facts', 'concepts' and 'skills' — somewhere in his thinking they all run together as 'information'.

The whole-class element of this lesson was enthralling. The emphasis on presentation/composition pays off. But some of these notes suggest an over-reliance on petty detail.

APPROACHES TO LESSON ANALYSIS

The lesson which the caseworker has just described was one of a sequence by Mr Prince observed as part of this project's study of topic work. Collecting data of this kind requires certain skills — a sharp professional insight, an eye for detail and so on — but is not too difficult. Analysing the materials calls for a different set of abilities. Here the casestudy worker must systematise his looking rather than empathise with what is happening, to probe rather than record. We found it easier to do this if we analysed the same lesson several times over, each time looking for clues about how the teacher tackled a particular skill or process. Initially, then, one had to read all the case-studied lessons to try to isolate those skills which seemed to require attention. In the lesson just quoted it is possible to work over the transcript several times and to look at one quite specific skill each time. The skills which appear to us to be most importantly illustrated in this lesson are as follows:

1. The managing skills of the teacher. There are references to the behaviour of pupils, to registration, to dealing with an interruption by the ancillary worker. By collecting together these references some perception can be gained of the smoothness of the classroom management in progress. Since this issue has been examined in chapter 6 it is included here for completeness, but managing skills will not be discussed further in this chapter.

2. The skill of handling teaching modes. The changes in teaching mode during the lesson are indicated in the caseworker's account. By following the notes of time in the margin of the account it is possible to get a very clear idea of the relative proportions of time which are devoted to any of the modes used. Again, this issue has been discussed in chapter 6, and is included here only to demonstrate how a rounded picture of the lesson can be built up. The matter will not be discussed at length in this chapter.

3. The skill of task-setting. When the lesson began, pupils were already engaged on tasks. These tasks are listed by the caseworker and a picture of them is built up from the teacher–pupil interchanges in the first half of the lesson. Thus we can begin to analyse this teacher's skills in task-setting and to discover something of his expectations about pupils' task-performance.

4. The skill of explaining. The second half of this lesson is didactic in style: the teacher dominates the proceedings with a lengthy input of information, in fact an explanation about certain physical laws and their importance. If this section of the lesson is to be successful then the explanation must be clear. Given that we can isolate some

191

criteria for effective explaining, then the quality of this explanation can be judged.

5. *The skill of questioning.* Prior to, and during, the exposition of Newton's discoveries, the teacher asks questions. Questioning, like explanation and the setting of tasks, is a recurrent activity in topic lessons and a crucial teaching skill, therefore. In this case the questions asked can be isolated and can be subjected to scrutiny, thus providing another perspective on the overall effectiveness of this lesson.

6. *The skill of evaluating learning.* The other major teacher-activity recorded in this lesson is that of monitoring and judging the learning which is taking place. Thus the teacher walks round looking at pupils' work, pulling them up for errors, advising, and eventually intervening for the benefit of the whole class. This is another recurrent skill in topic lessons, but it will not be discussed here since a whole chapter, chapter 8, will be devoted to it in due course.

So, we can summarise. The various strands of this lesson can be grouped under six areas of teaching skill. Of these, the first two have been discussed at length in another context, and the last is dealt with separately in chapter 8. In this chapter we shall concentrate on three skills, therefore: explaining, questioning and task-setting. Our next task will be to review this reported lesson in more detail in order to examine the teacher's skills in these three critical areas.

The skill of explaining

In our transcript of Mr Prince's lesson, explanation occupies the segment that runs from 1.45 p.m. until 2.10 p.m. — a block of twenty-five minutes. This is a considerable proportion of the lesson allocation, and clearly to be an effective use of learning time the explanation must be skilfully handled. How can one judge whether this is so or not?

It would take another whole book to justify and establish a set of criteria for judging effective explanations. Luckily, we do not have to go to those lengths, for others (Brown and Hatton 1982) have done this for us. Their research has led them to suggest that the following might be some useful criteria for assessing explaining skills:

The use of language

1. The teacher controls vocabulary and sentence structure; pupils

are invited to put ideas into their own words; vague terms and complex qualifications are avoided.

2. Gestures and voice are employed to emphasise important ideas; significant points are repeated or cued directly.

3. Pupils are invited to identify important ideas; their ideas are accepted and appropriately reinforced. Where possible, pupil contributions are used or paraphrased.

The explaining process

1. Each new point to be explained is introduced.

2. Appropriate examples in sufficient quantity are given.

3. Pupils are invited to provide examples from their own experience.

4. The teacher's selected examples are concrete, clear, apt.

5. Visual etc. aids are selected with the group's needs in mind.

6. Pupils are involved in manipulating materials or aids.

7. Significant points are progressively summarised.

8. Links between parts of the explanation are established.

9. Questions are asked to gauge understanding.

10. Pupils are free to raise questions or difficulties, and to express their feelings.

11. The pace of the explanation fits pupils' needs.

12. The level of thought is changed in response to pupils' level of understanding.

13. Overall approaches are modified when little pupil progress is evident.

Now is the time when an analysis of explaining skill in this lesson can be attempted. Indeed, you might like to break off at this point and, using these criteria, re-read the account of Mr Prince's lesson in order to assess his skill as an explainer. When you have done this you can read on to see whether your views accord with those of the present authors.

In order to examine explaining skill in this lesson what we have done is to re-write Brown and Hatton's criteria in the form of questions, for example, 'Did the teacher control vocabulary and sentence structure?' To each question we have given an answer, and then we have tried to illustrate that judgement from the text. All this appears as Table 7.1. Not all the features of an explanation listed in Table 7.1 need to appear in every explanation, of course; but by ticking off whether the feature occurred we can gain an immediate insight into the quality of the explanation given by Mr Prince beginning from the point in the text marked at 1.45 p.m.

Table 7.1: The use of language

Components of an effective explanation	Yes/ No	Comments in parentheses; or examples of use in quotation marks
Did the teacher		
1. control vocabulary and structure?	Yes	(Language intelligible; sentences short and to the point)
2. allow pupils to put ideas into own words?	Yes	'They'll speed up' 'Return rockets'
3. avoid vague terms?	Yes	(NB 'retro-rockets' explained)
4. employ gestures?	No	(No evidence from transcript)
5. repeat or cue significant points?	Yes	'This is important . . .'
6. let pupils identify important ideas?	Yes	'They'd get pulled down and and crash'
7. accept and use pupils' ideas?	Yes	'What about this gravity thing?' 'It's a force pulling things down to earth.'

The explaining process

8. introduce each new point?	No	(Links between parts of the explanation are made through responses to questions.)
9. give appropriate examples?	Yes	(Plenty of examples)
10. allow pupils to provide examples from experience?	Yes	'They floated around in the ship.'
11. make examples concrete, clear, apt?	Yes	(Examples diagrammatic; the pupils understand them)
12. make visual aids appropriate?	Yes	(Blackboard diagrams)
13. allows pupils to manipulate materials?	No	(Does not apply)
14. summarise significant points?	No	
15. establish links?	Yes	(Between gravity of a mountain, gravity in space — cannon balls, flight, etc.)
16. ask questions to gauge understanding?	Yes	(A string of questions, especially those which ask pupils to *apply* knowledge (the last 3 or 4))
17. make pupils free to question, contribute?	Yes/ No	(Pupils contribute freely but do raise questions spontaneously. One pupil who raises an objection ('It says here someone else invented the telescope') is brushed aside)

Table 7.1: contd.

Components of an effective explanation	Yes/ No	Comments in parentheses; or examples of use in quotation marks
18. pace the explanation appropriately?	Yes	(No direct evidence in the transcript; the fact that pupils understand suggests this is so.)
19. change level in response to pupils' needs?	Yes	(After 'How does the vehicle change direction?' there is an incorrect response. Teacher changes tack with new example.)
20. modify approach when little progress evident?	No	(Does not apply)

Fifteen features of an effective explanation out of a list of twenty are to be found in our transcript. This teacher appears to be a good explainer, with a firm grasp of this skill.

The skill of questioning

There are a number of ways in which questions can be categorised in order to allow us to explore their effectiveness. Some of these methods are very simple, others quite complicated. Here we shall concern ourselves with just two possible analyses, the first a very straightforward one.

A widespread method of categorising questions is by use of the bi-polar system of calling questions either 'closed' or 'open'. Closed questions are capable of being answered very briefly, usually in a word or two; the answer is likely to be factual and has normally been predetermined by the questioner. For example, this exchange:

Teacher. What do we call this symbol?
Pupil. A crotchet.
Teacher. How many beats is it worth?
Pupil. One.

would be regarded as consisting of two closed questions.

Open questions often begin with words like 'How?' and 'Why?'

Table 7.2: Questioning skills analysed

Open or closed		The question	Level of cognitive demand
C		What's wrong with this?	0
C		It's not the drawing: what's wrong with it?	0
C		A nice drawing, but what's wrong with it?	0
C		That's a complicated border isn't it?	0
C		How about a title?	0
C		Have you looked through the list?	0
C		Are there any names you recognise?	0
C		Is that Concorde?	0
C		Has anyone else written about Concorde?	0
	O	Why Concorde: what's important about it?	2
C		Is there anything in the reference books about Concorde or supersonic aircraft?	0
C		Have you looked at that list yet?	0
C		What's going to be the main colour?	0
C		No — what kind of country is it?	2
C		Who are you going to write about?	0
	O	What do you know about Faraday?	1
C		What was the subject we studied before?	0
C		Who was he?	1
	O	But what about this gravity thing?	1
C		What do we call this — not a pull?	1
C		Which (cannon ball or marble) would hit the ground first?	1
C		Who disagrees?	0
C		Who thinks that?	0
C		Was Newton right?	1
	O	How did the spacemen demonstrate this lessening pull?	3
C		As they get nearer the sun what will happen?	3
C		When they're descending, what do they have to do?	3
C		What sort of motors?	1
C		What does that mean?	2
	O	How does the vehicle change direction?	3
C		What would happen if this vehicle went too slowly?	3
C		If John shot a cannon, what would happen?	3
	O	What happens if a satellite slows down?	3
C		Has this happened?	1
	O	Suppose . . . you were to accelerate it?	3

			Low 77%	0	16	46%
				1	8	23%
C = 28 80%				2	3	8%
O = 7 20%			High 25%	3	8	23%
35 Questions				4	0	0%
				5	0	0%
				6	0	0%
					35	

196

They ask pupils to go beyond stating a fact or recalling a piece of knowledge; the answers cannot be predetermined; the responses are, of necessity, usually of a sentence or more in duration.

In Table 7.2 the questions asked during this lesson by Mr Prince are listed and the left-hand column indicates to which of these two categories the question belongs.

A more complicated analysis is based on the classic work by Benjamin Bloom (1956) and is designed to explore the level of thinking or cognitive demand implicit in the question. The analysis (in a modified version after Kerry 1982) consists of seven categories; and while the categories do not form a hierarchy they can be divided into low-demand and high-demand questions. The categories are as follows:

0 managing	
1 recall	Low order
2 simple comprehension	
3 application	
4 analysis	Higher order
5 synthesis	
6 evaluation	

In Table 7.2 each of Mr Prince's questions is assigned to one of these categories, as shown in the right-hand column. If we examine the information gleaned from the analysis in Table 7.2, Mr Prince's questioning skills can now be explored.

The most striking finding is that 80 per cent of the questions asked by Mr Prince are closed, i.e. he has predetermined the answer he requires and is satisfied with a brief response. If one accepts that pupils are more likely to deduce, reason and try out ideas in response to open questions rather than closed ones, then this simple analysis has already put its finger on something quite important. The more detailed breakdown which it is possible to make using the adapted Bloomian categories helps to explain the imbalance between open and closed questions.

Looking at the right-hand column of Table 7.2 we see that Mr Prince begins with a long series of questions which are really concerned not with learning as such but with managing that learning. The long opening sequence of 24 questions is punctuated twice by comprehension questions and six times by data-recall questions. By this point in the lesson he has reached the stage where he has decided to intervene in order to pursue the idea of Newton's contribution to modern space travel. Now the question sequence is dominated by interrogatives designed to see whether the pupils can apply the principles associated with the law of gravity to television films they have seen about space travel. The whole cognitive demand of the lesson is raised at this point, the three most important questions in this learning sequence being analysis questions formulated in an open-ended way:

How does the vehicle change direction?
What happens if a satellite slows down?
Suppose you were . . . to accelerate it?

In examining the pupils' answers to these questions Mr Prince can discover what level of learning is taking place in the class.

So, how effective is his question technique? Of course, it would be impossible for all classroom questions to be at a high cognitive level. What is important is for teachers to monitor the proportion of high-level questions to low-level ones; in this case 23 per cent to 77 per cent. But the analysis clearly shows three strategies for improving this balance. First, to find ways to replace some of the managing questions that predominate early on by questions designed to explore pupils' learning. Second, that the teacher should become more conscious of how questions are phrased so that he exploits the potential of open questions. Third, no questions in this lesson fell into the categories 'analysis', 'synthesis' and 'evaluation'; so perhaps Mr Prince should be reading messages here about introducing more variety into his higher-level questioning.

Of course this analysis is based upon one lesson only, and to be effective would have to be repeated, since a single lesson may be untypical of a teacher's normal mode of working. But the technique can be adapted easily by any teacher with enough interest to tape record his or her own lesson, subsequently to write down each question, and to code it in the manner shown. The point of skills training lies less in trying to get teachers to conform to one pattern of behaviour and more in raising self-awareness about one's own classroom practice.

The skill of task-setting

Next, we turn to task-setting and explore how this skill can be examined. There are two main pieces of information the teacher needs to know about the task: first, its target (i.e. whether it is set to the whole class, to a group or to an individual); and second, the level of cognitive demand made by the task (this being a similar kind of analysis to that applied to questions in the previous section).

The matter of deciding on the target is usually quite simple, and an obvious coding system would be:

WC for tasks set to the whole class
G for tasks set to a group
I for tasks set to an individual

This code is shown in the bottom right-hand column of Table 7.3 for the lesson described above.

Table 7.3: Task analysis sheet

Topic: Great Britain

Background to the task
The teacher has provided a list of areas which relate to the theme (e.g. inventors, monarchs, historical events, etc.). Pupils choose subjects from the list, read about the chosen topic, make notes. A fair copy of work is written up into a topic folder.

Tasks in progress

1. Written work in topic folders.	L and H
2. Consulting and condensing information from books.	L and H
3. Drawing in topic folders.	L
4. Decorating the margins of written pages.	L

Context of task (WC, G or I)
Each pupil has been free to choose his/her subject matter within specified limits, but all the pupils are engaged on the same task processes as described above. There is no systematic attempt to modify these processes to individual abilities.   WC

The most simple method of assessing cognitive demand is once again on a bi-polar scale: high (H) or low (L). This analysis is also shown in the right-hand column of Table 7.3. Low-level tasks would consist of copying, drawing, simple collection of data, revision and reinforcement activities. High-level tasks involve *using* knowledge (applying it, deducing from it, reasoning, evaluating) or require empathy (imaginative reconstruction, 'creative' writing, etc.).

If we lay out the tasks set in Mr Prince's lesson in the way indicated in Table 7.2 then a simple analysis of the kind indicated can be carried out.

What we find is that, while pupils may in practice proceed on tasks at their own pace and level, no allowance for this is built into the task by the teacher; and thus we are dealing with individual learning in a whole-class setting, not with individualised learning. Two of the task activities in progress are low level: they both consist of drawing. The other two can proceed at either a low level (pupils read a passage, then copy it out without much understanding), or at a high level (pupils read a range of source materials, select, précis and produce their own slant in a final account).

On the task front, therefore, the lesson appears to be a busy one, with children able to use some discretion about what research to do, to choose their own pace, and to operate at their own level. The hidden skill of the teacher is to know each pupil's capacity and to keep him up to it or to extend it. This might effectively be done through monitoring when pertinent questions about the learning might be asked of individuals — a point made in the previous section about questioning skills.

THE INFLUENCE OF TEACHING CONTEXT

So we have now explored a single lesson in considerable detail, looking specifically at three teaching skills — explaining, questioning and task-setting. We have noted particular strengths in the teaching, and some areas where perhaps the teacher might explore modifications to his techniques. We have *not* made a judgement about whether this was a good lesson or a bad one — that was not the purpose of the breakdown of skills. What we have done is to form a more *detailed* picture of a lesson in progress so that we do not have to rely on intuitive judgements about the effectiveness of the lesson. In making any ultimate decision about our view of the teacher's performance here we would need to know a little more about the kind of school with which we are dealing. To illustrate this, perhaps you would now like to answer the question: how effective was the teaching evidenced in this caseworker's account of a lesson? When you have formulated your response to this question, read the following paragraphs. They are a description of the school given to the caseworker by the head. When you have read these paragraphs ask yourself whether you want to revise your judgement about the teaching in any way.

Extract from a case-study worker's notebook

Summary of an interview with the head teacher of Moore Cove Middle (8–12) School

CSW. Tell me about the background to the school.

H. A small number of bright pupils.
A largish number of slow learners.
A council estate school.
This was the first estate built after the war.
Many original families still here.
Leads to stable relations between families and school.
About 1965 it was proposed that the school should be an SPA school.
H. fought SPA, despite financial advantages, to avoid labelling.
Opted for SED — exceptional difficulty.
In past, some extra staffing and (in past) some extra money.
But in last 2½ years all this advantage has gone.
Immediately after war the school very full.
About 1954 Erskine School built — numbers dropped.
But recently a new private housing estate and pupils are now coming from there on recommendation and reputation.
This is boost to staff morale.
Fifteen per cent pupils are now from beyond the immediate estate and the intake is becoming more balanced.
But problems still with us: often it's like sitting on a powder keg.
It is now easier for bright pupils — they are less swamped, and those children now are becoming leaders in work and behaviour.
Because of this we can give more help and time to the disturbed pupils.
This means an all-round gain for pupils.

CSW. Can you spell out what social disadvantage means here; for instance does it mean a high criminal area, a broken-home syndrome?

H. Many heads could list factors like broken homes. But here it begins from the base of two inadequate people marrying and having lots of children.
Parents are often inadequate.
Twelve years ago even, many dads were unemployed.
Mostly they are unskilled fathers.
Poor home management by wives.
Violence in the home.

201

Cohabitation.

Incest common.

Intermarriage of cousins; half-cousins.

Sadly, many fathers commit suicide or die of heart-failure at 35–45 years because of family pressures.

Many pupils are motherless, often due to cervical cancer.

Diet is a factor: fish and chips and coke; irregular meals.

Parents have children very young, often pre-marriage.

Mothers often don't pursue proper post-natal care because of family pressures.

Tight-knit community means when broken marriages occur they are the cause of much tension to youngsters in school.

TEACHING SKILLS: A SUMMARY

The purpose of this chapter and the previous one has been to identify and isolate some teaching skills; we have selected some key skills — managing, handling teaching mode, explaining, questioning and task-setting. This done, we have explored some criteria for judging teachers' performance on them and have illustrated how these criteria can be applied by using extracts from the case studies. One important area of teaching skill, that of evaluating learning, is reserved for the next chapter; but we are now able to review those questions about skills raised in chapter 3 and repeated on p. 182. Clearly, we have defined the skills and shown up procedures for reviewing them that can lead the practitioner on to systematic skill development, either by using a tape recording of his own lessons or by getting together with like-minded colleagues to scrutinise one another's practice. In the case-studied lesson we have seen a variety of skills employed, in a blend which sustained pace and interest: the caseworker reported his own and the pupils' considerable enthusiasm for the lesson. Finally, we have seen in the lesson account how the teacher managed transitions in the style, tempo and activities of the lesson as they changed rapidly in the light of the teacher's response to what he felt to be a need for the pupils to apply knowledge about a historical figure (Newton) to their world (space travel). You might care to explore how the insights gained in chapters 6 and 7 have helped you in your ability to analyse lessons. Lesson accounts on pp. 48–56 and pp. 79–80 of this book lend themselves to analysis of the kind described.

In these two chapters on classroom processes, it is suggested, we have come close to the heart of the teacher's daily world and have done so in a way that can provide scope for real professional development. It is to this last issue that we now turn in this chapter.

DEVELOPING PROFESSIONALISM

In chapter 3, we posed these questions:

Questions about professional development

How, and how often, do you monitor teaching processes in your own classroom?

How can individual teachers become more self-analytical about their practice?

How can they help each other towards this analytical approach?

What is the role and function of in-service training here? How can it operate effectively?

It has to be said that few teachers monitor their own teaching in any systematic way; but chapters 6 and 7 have provided some possible answers to the first two questions here. Furthermore, we have hinted at the need for individual teachers to get together to monitor their skills. On the final question, some general observations are included in our concluding chapter. To draw this chapter to a close perhaps it is opportune to quote from a case study in which a head teacher is describing his own approach to in-service training:

CSW. You've implied a balanced curriculum here is largely achieved through the professionalism of the teacher.

BP. True; but it takes effort. The school is large, so it's subdivided. We have four year groups, with year-group leaders. But there's also some planning between the year groups. This goes on informally in the staffroom. But we have one staff training night each week: there's a constant looking at our curriculum across the school.

CSW. That's a vertical management structure. Can you describe a staff training evening?

BP. The pattern is variable. Recently we looked at art and craft: its use in other areas of the curriculum and at the specific skills it should develop. Two talented artists ran six sessions for the other staff: mainly practical work, so the work could be used in the classroom. *They bring back and discuss what happens when they try ideas out. Topics for scrutiny are chosen by the staff. If we reach a hiatus I might put in an idea, but it's quite rare for me to need to intervene.*

CSW. Now let's look at horizontal management, how the year-group leaders communicate.

BP. Through frequent meetings. That's where really the nitty-gritty takes place. Historically we had a more formalised structure. But now the people themselves take over. I don't attend these meetings — that helps them to be informal. I meet year-group leaders weekly and they bring me items that need discussion.

CSW. So the two systems mesh together?

BP. Yes. But periodically I sample to check that things are going on quite well. The head's role is to lead but not cajole; I can do this formally or informally by sampling. So I spend most mornings in classrooms talking to the teachers; and I can get an idea of what's happening.

CSW. When did you last have a new teacher join the staff?

BP. Recently — a temporary appointment.

CSW. How do new people get drawn into these structures?

BP. Because it's happening; and they do do some of their own things. We avoid pressure; we prefer conviction. The younger teacher may be primarily concerned with class management and confidence. Later they can look at content; though the two are interrelated. Also, they talk informally; members of staff include them in activities; they go to evening social activities. It's a relationship process.

8

Record-keeping and Assessment

In chapter 7 we looked at ways in which our case histories on topic work in action could be analysed in order to illuminate teachers' skills. One of the skills we identified there was the skill of task setting. This chapter tries to come to terms with some aspects of the complicated business of task analysis, and the theme is pursued into chapter 9. The matter is raised in the context of the need for schools and teachers to keep effective records of pupils' progress in topic lessons and their often reported failures to do so, or to do so effectively.

It might be opportune to recapitulate at this point on the issues about record-keeping that were highlighted in chapter 3. These were as follows:

Given that you have identified your intentions for any given topic and selected appropriate teaching methods, how do you evaluate the pupils' achievements?

Do you evolve methods for tracking the progress they have made

in attitudes to learning?
conceptually?
in learning information?
in social learning?
in acquiring practical skills?
in handling language?
in study skills?
in presenting information?
in making judgements?
in making decisions about their own work and

independence?

How is each of these items monitored?

How is each child's progress recorded?

What use do you make of the information yourself?

Do you check over the records when you

review each child's work?
talk to the pupils about their work?
plan possible next steps?
plan remedial or stimulation exercises?
consider next term's syllabus?
write reports for parents or head?

Do you communicate the information collected to anyone else? To whom? The head teacher? Other staff? The teacher who takes over the class for the next school year? Parents?

How is the information communicated? Do you amend or edit it in any way? How? Why?

Is there some overall system in the school for pooling evaluation and assessment data for planning purposes? How does this system work? Could it be improved?

Above all, do you use your knowledge of pupils' progress in learning to feed back to the pupils themselves, on a regular basis, ideas about how they can improve their own classroom performance, skills and attitudes?

These, then, were the questions to emerge from the case studies and to which we tried to find answers in the studied schools. These are the questions which we will be asking you to address (comparing what is written here with your own practice) in chapters 8 and 9. These are the questions which we shall attempt to illuminate in what follows. However, it should be said at the outset that we have already drawn attention to the fact that our case studies found rather less helpful professional practice in this area than in others covered in this book. Inevitably, then, we shall draw rather more on the researches of others in these chapters and proportionately less upon our own case-study data. Where possible we shall still draw examples from our own data, but the reader should be ready for a change of mood in the following pages: a change from exegesis of current good (or even bad) practice to one of more tentative speculation.

It does not take much imagination to see that, if each day you arrived at school to be faced with a new class of pupils whom you had never seen before, the task of teaching would be virtually impossible. Sustained contact with the same pupils is necessary in order to establish a working relationship with the class and the individuals which comprise it and to develop some understanding of their interrelationships, and also to generate productive transactions likely to contribute to pupils' intellectual or social education. Such contact requires some knowledge of their educational history.

The question of what information would enable a teacher to plan an appropriate curriculum, to devise appropriate teaching strategies and to intervene tactically in effective ways is central to any consideration of record-keeping. In ideal circumstances, a record of pupils' curricular histories would be written and continuously updated, including an account of the sequence of learning events which each had experienced and their responses to these events. As with all histories, these accounts would include both a *description* of such events in terms of their most obvious features (such as subject matter), and *interpretations* of their educational significance (such as their contribution to developing conceptual maps which give these events generalisable meanings). Also, the historical record would indicate the kinds and levels of intellectual engagement in these learning experiences.

The Upper Junior Mathematics record on pp. 208–11 was one example collected during a Schools Council survey of record-keeping described by Phil Clift (1981), and it satisfies most of the criteria implied by the above description.

A teacher receiving a pupil whose mathematical 'concepts and experience' had been the subject of such a record as that shown on pp. 208–11 would be informed, for example, that he or she had experienced the measurement of *length* in metric units in practical contexts and correlated these measurements with the application of the 'four rules' to decimals. Presumably the headings 'Intro.' and 'Checked' refer to the fact that this work has been done and completed with some (unspecified) success. The comments column allows for the recording of description, if not diagnosis, of particular difficulties. It is, however, best to regard this as an examplar of a record of *work done* rather than a record of *achievement* — because there are no explicit criteria of achievement specified. It is, for example, possible that a pupil may in section 10, 'The whole and its parts', divide fractions by the routine application of the algorithm 'turn the divisor upside down and multiply', with no understanding of how this

Junior Mathematics Record

Name of child ....   Date of birth ....

Mathematical concept and experience	Intro.	Checked	Checked	Checked	Comments
NUMBER					
1. Recognition of numbers and recording in words and figures					
.... 1,000					
.... 1,000,000					
Order of size — extent to include					
fractions and decimals					
Simple arithmetic series					
2. Revision and extension of 4 rules					
Mathematical language, e.g. product, etc.					
Addition					
Subtraction					
Multiplication — simple extending using 2 or 3 figs					
Division — simple extending to use 2 figs					
3. Place value (revision)					
4. Use of other bases (Dienes) in 4 rules 2					
3					
5					
5. Mental practice in addition and subtraction — 100					
6. Multiplication and division facts (stress relationships) e.g. $3 \times 8 = 24$					
$8 \times 3 = 24$					
$24 \div 3 = 8$					
$24 \div 8 = 3$					
7. Odd and even numbers					
8. Prime numbers (use AEM) including positive and negative nos and zero					
9. Square numbers (use AEM)					

Mathematical concept and experience	Intro.	Checked	Checked	Comments
NUMBER				
10. THE WHOLE AND ITS PARTS				
Practical work in fractional parts ¼, ½, ¾, 1/5, 1/10, etc.				
Addition				
Subtraction				
Multiplication				
Division				
11. DECIMALISATION				
Meaning of the decimal point				
Addition to 3 places				
Subtraction to 3 places				
Simple multiplication to 2 places				
Long multiplication extended to 3 places				
Simple division to 2 places				
Long division by 2 figures (e.g. 26)				
12. PERCENTAGES (correlate with 10 and 11)				
13. MONEY				
Handling and changing				
Addition				
Subtraction				
Multiplication				
Division				
14. LENGTH (metric)				
Extension of practical work in mm, m and km				
Mental facts — mm, cm, m and km				
Correlate with 4 rules in decimals				

Mathematical concept and experience	Intro.	Checked	Checked	Comments
15. WEIGHT (metric)				
Extension of practical work in grammes and kg				
Mental facts — gm, kg and metric tonne				
16. CAPACITY AND VOLUME (metric)				
Extension of practical work in ml and litres				
Mental facts — ml and litres				
Correlate with 4 rules in decimals				
17. TIME, DISTANCE AND SPEED				
Extension of practical work				
Mental facts (using abacus) — sec, min, hr, days				
Calendar months and years (incl. leap year)				
24-hr clock, timetables				
Journeys (speed and distance)				
Universal time — rotation of earth — time change				
18. GRAPHS				
Histograms, straight line conversion				
Correlation with previous experience				
19. AVERAGES				
20. SHAPE				
Various shapes, perimeters				
Area — square, rectangle and triangle				
Volume — cubes and cuboids				
Angles in shapes — right angle				
acute angle				
obtuse angle				
21. RATIO				

Mathematical concept and experience	Intro.	Checked	Checked	Checked	Comments
22. SIMPLE ALGEBRAIC EQUATIONS (Use balance at outset)					
23. SETS EXTRA EXPERIENCE [½ page allowed for list]					

procedure effects the division (e.g. in the case of 3/4 ÷ 1/5: how does 3/4 × 5/1 tell you how many fifths there are in 3/4?).

In this record, descriptions of content seem quite adequate for practical purposes, but descriptions of the kinds and levels of intellectual engagement are perhaps less so. Nevertheless there are indications that, in some cases, practical work will be done and, as in section 11, decimalisation, limits to the expected achievements are stated. In terms of developed conceptual maps a good deal might be inferred from this record; but as the record is organised in terms of topics rather than concepts there can be no guarantee that the pupil whose record includes a 'checked' item has developed the related concept(s).

It is interesting to compare the above record with the concept maps produced by the Nuffield Mathematics Project 5 to 13, given in the series of booklets called *Checking-up* (published by Chambers and John Murray, 1973). These and similar maps were produced by the authors of *Checking-up*, who were from the Institut des Sciences d'Education in Geneva under the general supervision of Piaget. These are *concept maps*, not records of either work done or achievement. Concepts are described by the authors of these maps as 'ideas which are abstracted from experience', so that, for example, 'number' is a concept, and so are 'addition', 'sorting', 'inclusion', 'ordering' and 'mass'. Moreover they assert: 'A concept cannot be taught, it is acquired through the child's activity.' The map in Figure 8.1 should be read from top to bottom. It indicates a series of paths from 'pre-operational thought', through 'concrete operations' to the 'formal operations' associated with abstract thinking. Each box indicates a concept is present and is linked with other concepts in a network of logical relationships.

Apart from the strange omission of the concept 'time', this map circumscribes the conceptual structures required to understand elementary mathematics and their application. Despite the probable truth of the statement that concepts cannot be taught but are acquired through the child's experience, it is nevertheless possible to translate the concept map into a record of work done by constructing tasks which provide the *experiences* upon which conceptual growth may depend. Moreover, by observing pupils' responses to such experiences it is possible to monitor conceptual development. Indeed it was for this purpose that the *Checking-up* series was written.

Consider, for example, the concept of 'ordering' in mathematics; that is to say, with respect to some variable scalar property objects can be ranked in order. A series of tasks may be devised which make increasingly greater demands on pupils in ways which provide pupils with the opportunity to develop and elaborate the concept of ordering, and teachers with the means of monitoring its development. Examples would be:

Task 1. Pupils are given seven *red* cylinders *of equal diameters* but of different lengths. They are asked to set them out on a table in a row according to length, the longest one at one end, the shortest at the other.

This task could be varied by using different materials (milkstraws or pencils) or different colours, or different cross-sections, both shapes and diameters. All except length would be held constant for any one task. At least one task would include the interesting case where the diameter was greater than the length.

Task 2. Another variable would be chosen, such as mass (in practice weight) and pupils would be provided with seven *blue* cylinders *of equal length* and the *same diameter* but made of materials with different densities and be asked to rank them so that the one with the greatest mass (weight) was ranked No. 1 and the one with the least mass (lightest) ranked No. 7. This task could be carried out by using a direct reading balance when the absolute weight of each cylinder may be determined, but the teacher's insight into the pupils' developing concepts would be enhanced if such a balance were used which allowed only comparative weights to be determined, i.e. that cylinder D was heavier than cylinder A, and so on.

Task 3. In the above cases the tasks have been so contrived that only one property varies at a time. In this task, rather than using fundamental measurements, derivative measurements are used such as speed, volume and density. Thus as volume varies so will diameter and/or length; as speed varies so will distance and/or time, and so on.

In this task seven *yellow* cylinders are provided, each of a different volume such that ranking by neither diameter nor length would produce a correct ranking by volume. Pupils would be required to rank the cylinders such that the one with the largest volume be ranked No. 1 and that with the smallest volume No. 7.

Ranking the speed of mechanically propelled toys could be a productive practical task in this context, too. Unlike the volume task, where the variables length and diameter of each cylinder are fixed,

213

Figure 8.1: A conceptual map

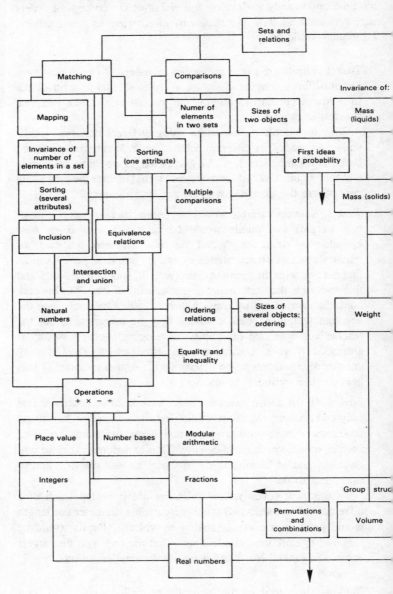

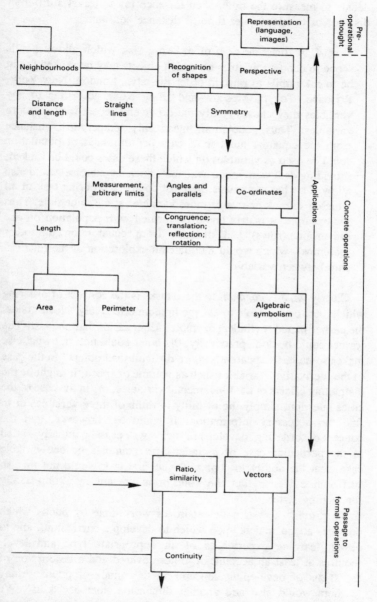

Source: Nuffield Mathematics Project 5 to 13, *Checking-up 3* (Chambers and John Murray, 1973), p. 212.

here it would be possible for pupils to control variables. They might decide to measure the time taken for each toy to travel a different distance or to keep either time or distance constant.

Task 4. A different type of ordering task which allows pupils scope to choose variables on which objects may be ranked might be to ask pupils to rank in order the cities London, New York, Brisbane, Tokyo, Moscow and Hong Kong according to any variables they chose, justify the order and repeat for two more variables. Thus population, mean July temperature, distance from the equator, number of cars per thousand of population could be used as variables on which these cities could be ranked, providing data were made available. Such an exercise would also allow for what is perhaps the most complex ordering task of all which is to rank on two or more variables at the same time. Thus for example, a matrix could be formed with population on one dimension (rows) and distance from equator on the other (columns), which would facilitate an exploration of the relationship between variables.

Clearly what is *common* to these tasks is the concept of ordering which must be available to engage in them effectively. Nevertheless the earlier pencil (cylinder) examples seem easier than the last. The former could be done practically, the latter could not; but what else makes some tasks apparently more difficult than others? In the case of the 'derivative' variables such as volume or speed, it might be the distracting effects of the fundamental variables, or, in the case of the cities question, simply the inability to think of three variables or to find the necessary information. It could be, however, that the concept of 'ordering' develops in such a way as to be initially so tied to the particular case of cylinder-type examples or one-variable cases that the ability to cope with the first task would not furnish sufficient evidence that the concept is present in a universally functioning state.

To provide a systematic record of work done by pupils which provides adequate data upon which to develop a curriculum, and to design learning experiences of an appropriate type and level, requires at least an account of topics covered and a description of the status of developing concepts in the minds of pupils. Many teachers would also add another dimension, that of 'skills'. We found in our case studies that in relation to topic work so-called skills were identified as major components of the anticipated learned outcomes of teacher–pupil and particularly pupil–resource transactions. In one of the schools with which we collaborated a list of skills which in the staff's view were practised and developed through topic work included the following:

Comprehension skills:
skimming
looking for the main points
reading 'between the lines'
detecting bias in accounts

Observation skills
Recording skills:
note-taking
tabulation and drawing graphs
use of tape recorder
use of camera

This may be compared with the Assessment of Performance (Science) list of 'Categories of science performance' (Assessment of Performance Unit 1982), which for the Target Population age 11 was:

Main Categories	Sub-categories
1. Using symbolic representations:	Reading information from graphs, tables and charts. Expressing information as graphs, tables and charts.
2. Using apparatus and measuring instruments:	Using measuring instruments.
3. Using observation:	Using a branching key. Observing similarities and differences. Interpreting observations.
4. Interpretation and application:	Describing and using patterns in presented information. Judging the applicability of a given generalisation. Distinguishing degrees of inference. Making sense of information using science concepts.

                                       Generating alternative hypotheses.

5. Design of   Identifying or proposing testable
    investigations: statements.
                            Assessing experimental
                            procedures.
                            Devising and describing investigations.

6. Performance of
    investigations

While it is clear that the term 'skill' (which is often applied to the kinds of competencies listed above) eludes unambiguous definition, the lists do refer to observable, and hence recordable, behaviours in which pupils may be seen to engage during the performance on tasks of different kinds. Perhaps it is best, though not wholly satisfactory, to regard such 'skills' as thought processes which can become routinised with practice and which come to be carried out without conscious consideration of the nature of the processes involved.

It might help at this stage to provide an example of the kind of records of work done which might result from a lesson on submarines, part of the topic 'water' observed in one of the schools in which we collected case-study materials. Pupils read an account of the mechanism by which submarines can regulate their depth in water. Given a 'squeezy' bottle with two half-inch-diameter holes in one side but with a stopper firmly in place at the normal delivery end, a rubber tube and a sink almost full of water, they were invited to make the squeezy bottle mimic the floating and sinking action of the submarine. This work was done in groups of four to six pupils and a good deal of animated discussion took place about what to do, what happened, and how it could be explained. The teacher's function, having set up the task, was essentially consultative. This task could have been recorded in terms of topic as:

Floating and sinking: submarines

In terms of concepts, of which this topic has an abundance, the record might be:

gas; compression; mass; density; flotation; pumping

In terms of competencies or 'skills' the record would read:

Using observations — interpretation of observations;
Interpretation and application — making sense of information, using science concepts;
Design of investigations — devising and describing investigations;
Performance of investigations.

Making records of work done in topic work often poses a more difficult problem for teachers, especially when the topic takes on a multi-disciplinary nature. If the topic is not located in some discipline such as history or science it may appear to be conceptually fragmented. Take, for example, the 'forecast' of the topic 'water', produced by one of our teacher colleagues (Figure 8.2).

In her school the functions of such 'forecasts' were to negotiate with the head of the school the suitability of the topic with her class and as a basis for planning the tasks to be undertaken by her pupils. In this case this scheme was the only record of work done by the pupils on this topic. In addition, folders of pupils' work were retained but no other *record* was kept of either work done or achievement. This arrangement was by no means unique; in fact it was commonplace in our collaborating schools. In a larger survey, of 192 schools, Phil Clift found that the only curriculum categories included in records in more than 50 per cent of schools in his sample were 'Reading development' (96 per cent), 'List of mathematical topics covered' (81 per cent) and 'Social and personal development' (55 per cent).

This suggests that the concepts developed and skills acquired and practised apart from language and number work are not given the attention which, arguably, they deserve.

There are problems associated with this system of recording the 'content' of learning which will be discussed later. We may note at this point that a teacher receiving pupils who had been exposed to this curriculum, given this record, would have a picture of work covered. The picture varies in the details given, from fairly tightly related interconnected patterns — water cycle → evaporation → condensation → precipitation → weather — to open 'branches' such as 'literature'. The map does not pretend to represent more than content. The conceptual structures which might inform this content are not made explicit. It is however known from other information supplied by the teacher who drew this 'content map' that she has clear expectations about knowledge pupils are expected to gain,

Figure 8.2: Topic-work map: water

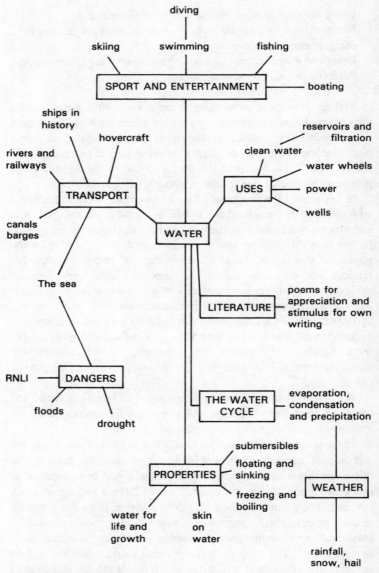

RESOURCES AVAILABLE

Books from county
library

skills to be practised, and attitudes fostered as a result of exposure to this project on water. These however were not subjected to *systematic observation*, and *records were not kept* of these outcomes of study.

A quite different approach to keeping a record of work done can be seen in the work of Neville Bennett and Charles Desforges on the quality of pupils' learning experiences in infant and primary classrooms (1984). Their concern was particularly with the *match* achieved between the nature of the tasks given to pupils and the ability of each pupil to engage effectively in that task. The main focus of their work is thus developmental, their interest being in the balance and sequence of demands made on pupils.

Records of work done may be restricted to description of the subject matter which forms the content of lessons: the previous records described are essentially of this type. But such accounts could be usefully augmented by reference to the *kinds of tasks* in which pupils are engaged. The problem here is that of finding a useful way of differentiating between tasks.

Bennett and Desforges, when investigating the quality of pupils' learning experiences in infant and primary classrooms, found it helpful to sort tasks into five classes: incremental, restructuring, enrichment, practice and revision. These can be described briefly as follows:

1. *Incremental tasks*. The acquisition and consolidation of *new* facts and skills, procedures, concepts or algorithms. 'If the key feature of the task is to focus on new material, even if the task involves much old material, then it is an incremental task.' Typically incremental tasks might require imitation of new models and/or step-wise reproduction of new procedures.

2. *Restructuring tasks*. Pupils are working with predominantly familiar materials but are required to discover, invent, or construct new ways of looking at problems or materials.

3. *Enrichment tasks*. Use of familiar knowledge in unfamiliar contexts. These tasks extend the range of application to concepts and skills (and to this degree add incrementally to the knowledge domain).

4. *Practice tasks*. Repetitive and rapid application of familiar knowledge and skills to familiar settings or problems. The object is not to acquire fact or skill or algorithm but to speed up and make automatic processes already in pupils' repertoire.

5. *Revision tasks*. Attention to materials or skills which have been

set aside for some time. Material is evoked which was once familiar.

This system of classification of tasks was devised in order to answer the question 'With respect to the learner's organisation of knowledge, what type of learning task is he being presented with?' i.e. to explore cases of matching and mismatching between the task given and the pupil's capacity to benefit from the task. It could also be used, however, to describe the frequency, range and even order of tasks given to pupils in a 'course of lessons' or topic.

In this system it is necessary to know, either from previous records or by investigation, the history of the pupils' exposure to the knowledge, concepts, procedures or algorithms under scrutiny.

If one wished to go beyond reporting the structure of a topic in terms of demands made by its component tasks (to the question 'What tasks will match a particular pupil's present competence?'), it would be necessary to extend the scope of the investigation to determine the learners' 'organisation of knowledge'. Records of this kind would seem to be indispensable if account were to be taken of pupils' achievements when assigning tasks.

Thus, it is easy to imagine a pupil with an interest in a particular topic in a class with less well-informed peers. In the absence of a record of this pupil's prior experience and achievement he may be set a task which for him is a *practice* or *revision* task but which for his classmates may be *incremental* or *restructuring*. Reference by HMI to 'failure to extend able pupils', and to other mismatching between present achievement and task set, presumably stems from a lack of teacher's knowledge of this critical component in task-setting. Such deficiencies could be reduced if appropriate records were kept. Later we will consider ways of describing achievement. At this stage, merely to describe 'content and nature and level of task demand' is being suggested as a beginning in the process of codifying information essential to achieve the purposes teachers wish to be served by records.

The Bennett system outlined above is by no means the only way by which tasks could be classified. His system concentrates on the individual pupil's learning history with reference to particular knowledge, skill, concept or algorithm. Alternatively, or possibly in conjunction with this scheme, one might differentiate between tasks by reference to the nature of the cognitive demands they make on pupils.

The means by which task-demands can be classified at different cognitive levels are not easy to invent. To achieve the ideal of totally unambiguous definitions and absolutely mutually exclusive categories, if this were possible, would be too complex an exercise and too time-consuming for present purposes. Practicality demands a simple system which may be 'rough' but will be 'readily' usable under classroom conditions. We may note in passing that Wynne Harlen (evaluator of the Science 5–13 project) used Bloom's *Taxonomy of Educational Objectives* (Bloom 1956) as a guide for planning lessons 'with objectives in mind'; and in a later project, 'Progress in learning science', a checklist of skills, concepts and attitudes was devised.

The two main problems associated with systems by which tasks might be classified, and thus form the basis of a record of work done, are:

how to devise and define categories in ways which facilitate ease of categorisation, and

how to invent rules which secure appropriate and consistent use of the categories.

A recurring difficulty in classifying tasks is that they are not usually devised with particular cognitive levels or stages in mind. Many tasks which we have seen reported in our case studies were apparently designed to motivate children to work. They were, in general terms, within the capacity of the pupils to respond appropriately, and, by engagement in them, they added to their store of knowledge about the topic and practised procedures and skills. In the process of completing the task new knowledge may have been acquired; or the way the task was set might have required some restructuring of the conceptual organisation in the pupils' minds and/or the application of such cognitive procedures as inferring or speculating. But these implications of any given task were not always clearly perceived at the setting stage. In reality, however, tasks are *complex* learning events which may make demands of *different* kinds with respect to the pupils' history, e.g. incremental/practice/revision, and at different cognitive levels.

To make a record of work done in a task and to 'sum' these records into a comprehensive record of work done in a topic is, therefore, extremely difficult. However, if we are prepared to compromise between a simple record and one which aims at minute comprehensiveness or unattainable precision, we may be able to make a type of record which can later be judged on the criterion of utility.

The following examples drawn from our case studies were tasks given to a third-year junior class working on a half-term topic — 'Roads'.

TASK I

Modern road building

(a) *Find out all you can about road-building.*

(b) *Write about all the different stages there are before a road is completed. (Draw pictures to illustrate your work.)*

(c) *Which people are involved?*

(d) *What machinery do they use?*

(e) *What signs or diversions might you see?*

(f) *Collect pictures and newspaper cuttings.*

You must use as many references as possible.

Make notes in your jotter first, then put your writing in the correct order and copy on to paper.

An important clue to the nature of the demands made by this task lies in the verbs which describe component activities. For the pupils, the central features of this task are reading descriptions about how roads are built, translating these descriptions into their own language and, guided by 'headings' given by the teacher, constructing an account illustrated with sketches (see Figure 8.3). Presumably one of the main outcomes of this task is that pupils will acquire factual information about road-building of which they were previously not aware, facts about how, from what materials, by what means, using what equipment, roads are made.

It is likely that in the process some facts of which they were previously 'aware' (possibly as disconnected bits of information) will be brought into some meaningful relationship. Thus in Bennett's terms *accretion* of facts and procedures may be accompanied by some *restructuring*, although one suspects the emphasis is on the former (see Table 8.1, p. 226).

In addition, there are demands upon the pupils' knowledge of vocabulary, of procedures (referring to indexes) and skills of comprehension, and of perception and communication in words and the task may be analysed as follows:

Figure 8.3: Analysis of Task I

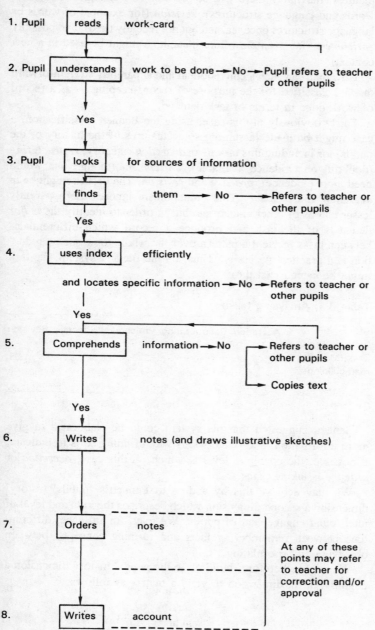

pictures. Inevitably there will be *practice* (for example of familiar words and language structures), *revision* (for example of words or language structures once learned but not recently used), and possibly *enrichment* (for example where metaphors might be used in a new context).

How then can such a conventional and apparently straightforward task be classified for the purpose of record-keeping — as a record of work done in terms of task-demand?

Fairly obviously in this case, using the Bennett classification, a case might be made (assuming some features of the history of the pupils) for including this task in an *accretion* category, *restructuring* (doubtful on evidence available), *enrichment* (though one would need more evidence), *practice* and *revision*. The best fit might be in *accretion* and *practice*. This reductionism ignores the apparently lesser claims of other categories, but in order to identify the *major* demands of the task and produce a record which differentiates between tasks to yield a pattern over the whole topic such a reduction is a practical necessity. Thus, on the Bennett system, the task might be categorised thus:

Table 8.1: Analysing tasks

	Accretion	Restructuring	Enrichment	Practice	Revision
Task: Modern road-building	×			×	

Bennett suggested that his system could be elaborated to give more information, and one obvious way of doing so is to indicate, if possible, the cognitive level at which, in this case, *accretion* or *practice* is taking place.

We may achieve this by adding to Bennett's 'pupils' history' dimension a second dimension which describes the kind and level of intellectual engagement of pupils. We may, for instance, differentiate between remembering facts and forming concepts, between observing and speculating.

We might, therefore, build on to the pupils' history dimension a cognitive level dimension to yield a matrix as follows:

Table 8.2: An enriched task-analysis model

Topic: Roads
Task: Modern road-building

Cognitive 'level'	Accretion	Restruc-turing	Enrich-ment	Practice	Revision
Procedures				×	
Facts	×				
Skills				×	
Concepts including explanations and reasons	×				
Principles including laws and generalisations					

Whereas the previous record (Table 8.1) informed us that something new had been introduced by this task (i.e. *accretion*), this version attempts to add more information — that both new *facts* and new *concepts* had been introduced.

The list of five cognitive categories in the left-hand column of Table 8.2 may be described thus:

Procedures. Ways of doing things, sequence of actions which achieve desired ends. They vary in complexity but can be manifest without the pupil necessarily understanding the rules of action: how to add up fractions or to write a sentence, to punctuate, to orientate a map, to read a thermometer, to set up a standard experiment, to look up a reference.

Facts. Information, including any statement known or believed to be true, about objects or phenomena now or in the past, including the names given to things.

Skills. Any appropriate action undertaken to secure facility, especially in this context referring to intellectual activities, e.g.

comprehension of text, diagrams and maps, graphs and other encoded information such as numbers, *inference*, seeing *logical connections* between data, *articulation* in language of ideas, and *description* of events and feelings.

Concepts including explanations and reasons. The connections between discrete events or objects to form sets or categories, especially between superficially different events or objects, e.g. force (falling objects, springs, explosions, jumping, jets, etc.).

Principles including laws and generalisations. General laws by which consistent action or understanding of natural phenomena can be achieved, e.g. 'democratic principles' and 'gravity'.

In the case of the task 'Modern road-building' (in the topic 'Roads') we could demonstrate that new *facts* were introduced and possibly new *concepts*, hence there would be two entries under the heading *accretion*. Obviously if we knew more about the particular books available to pupils and other possible sources of information we might add to the entries in this column. We might also have grounds for believing that some *restructuring* may occur in the minds of at least some pupils when the new facts which they have acquired induce a change in the meanings they have attached to their previously limited knowledge of road-building.

It is inevitable that some *procedures* will have been *practised*, and similarly *skills* — especially those associated with comprehension. The problem for the record-keeper is to decide whether these were *significant* elements in the task or, if you will, its main purpose.

Another task set during our case study by the same teacher in this third-year topic on 'Roads' is given below:

TASK II

Distances and Speed

1. *If you travelled at 50 mph, how long would it take you to do these distances:*
   (a) *Newcastle*   *to Dover*
               to Cardiff
               to Birmingham

(b) Carlisle   to *London*
                 to *Blackpool*
                 to *Bristol*

(c) Cardiff   to *Carlisle*
                 to *London*
                 to *Blackpool*

2. *Think about these next questions.*
   Remember 10 miles = 1/6 of 60 miles.
   What is 1/6 of 60 minutes?

   If you travelled at 60 mph, how long would it take you to do these distances:

   (a) Nottingham   to *Glasgow*
                        to *Edinburgh*
                        to *Bristol*
                        to *Cardiff*

   (b) London   to *Nottingham*
                      to *Glasgow*
                      to *Edinburgh*
                      to *Carlisle*
                      to *Dover*
                      to *Bristol*
                      to *Southampton*
                      to *Holyhead*

This task may be analysed as follows (mileage charts like those in the AA/RAC handbooks were available):

Figure 8.4: Analysis of Task II

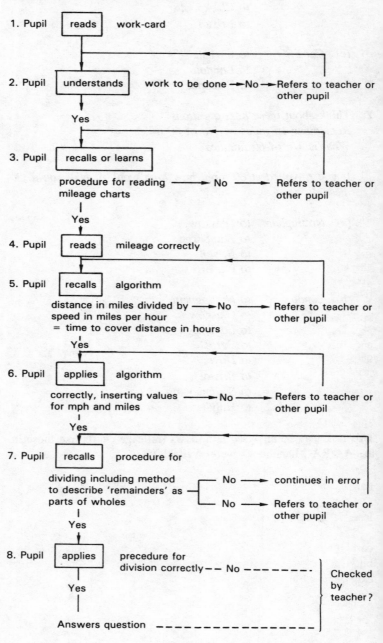

This task might be recorded as in Table 8.3.

Table 8.3: Analysis of Task II

Topic: Roads
Task: Distance and speeds

Pupils' history

Cognitive 'level'	Accretion	Restructuring	Enrichment	Practice	Revision
Procedures	×				×
Facts					
Skills			×		
Concepts including explanations and reasons					
Principles including laws and generalisations					

Accretion of procedures refers to pupils' use of the mileage chart, *revision of procedures* to the operation of division (distance ÷ speed). We have inferred from data supplied by the teacher that pupils learnt this procedure some considerable time previously, and *enrichment of skills* refers to the application of division to the particular problem of time/distance/speed relationships.

Other elements could have been recorded but were judged to be less significant in this particular task.

The third task which we have selected as an example from the case study not only demonstrated the procedures for classification but also suggests the unrealised potential of this task as a learning experience.

TASK III

Road-sign design

Aim. To find out which colour or colours show up best against other colours.

1. You will need to collect as many different coloured sheets of sugar paper as possible.
2. Use the letter stencils from the cupboard.
3. Cut out some circles and letters from the sugar paper.
4. Stick the letters on to the paper using as many different colour combinations as possible, e.g. red on yellow, black on white, green on orange, etc.
5. Make a list of your letter signs in your jotter, then take the signs and your jotter and pencil outside to see which sign shows up most clearly. Vary the distance 25m, 50m and 100m. Is the same sign clearly visible at each different distance?

This task may be analysed as follows:

Figure 8.5: Analysis of Task III

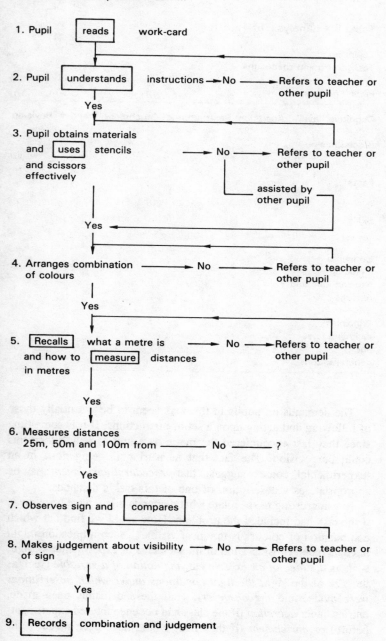

In grid form this might be recorded as in Table 8.4.

Table 8.4: Analysis of Task III

Topic: Roads
Task: Designing road signs

Pupils' history

Cognitive 'level'	Accretion	Restructuring	Enrichment	Practice	Revision
Procedures			×		
Facts					×
Skills					
Concepts including explanations and reasons					
Principles including laws and generalisations					

The demands on pupils in this task seem to be essentially those of following and acting upon a set of instructions. If it is some time since they last encountered the metre as a unit of length then this could be revision. The fact that measuring is being done in an 'experimental' context suggests that *procedural enrichment* may be appropriate as a description of one of this task's demands.

It is interesting to speculate what demands might have been made if the task had included the problem 'How could we find out which combination of colours is the most visible?' Such a question might have included consideration of the elements of experimental design, such as *the idea of an experiment*, *the notion of a variable* (such as the *size* of the sign, *the light conditions under which observations were made*, and *the observer*). Had these demands been made, entries under *accretion* (if the class had not encountered experiments before) or *enrichment* (if they had) would have been made in the *concepts* and *principles* squares.

Given that a teacher gave time and thought to producing records like the one described, then the audiences for records of this kind are (a) the teacher who made the record and (b) other teachers whose work with the pupils will relate to the work recorded. In order to make a record of work done according to this prescription, the teacher is required to know enough of a pupil's history to determine the column into which any task will be placed. Secondly, the teacher needs to have determined the level of cognitive demand made by the task set in order to locate the row in which the task is intended.

The teachers with whom we worked during our case studies without exception included in their plans for a topic statements of aims, objectives or intentions. However, it was not always evident how the tasks which they set related to these intentions. Sometimes this was due to vagueness in the way the intention was stated; for example 'to be aware of the dangers of too little or too much water' (in the topic 'Water'). On other occasions the tasks, although quite specific in their demands, could not easily be related to any stated intention, for example the time/distance/speed calculation in the topic 'Roads'.

A third classification problem, which stems from the way intentions were stated, is making the distinction between knowledge acquisition and concept formation. It may be that reference in the topic 'Water' to 'the danger of too much water' implies flooding, and that the conditions in which flood may occur will be considered. But can it be assumed that the relationship between the volume of water falling in a given time on a known area of the earth's surface will be compared with the volume of drainage channels, and account be taken of the porous nature of the land on to which it falls? Clearly the kind and level of intellectual demands which might be made in tasks stemming from intentions described in these terms is too variable to accurately translate intentions into tasks. A clearer statement of intent is required, particularly one which spells out the distinction between learning facts and learning (and learning to use) principles and generalisations.

A precondition for an accurate record of topic work done is to write a sufficiently comprehensive and detailed list of intentions. These may then be translated into tasks, each task being directed specifically at a particular intent. To classify a task, in effect, two questions are asked: *what* will the pupil learn? (a procedure? facts? a skill? a concept? a generalisation or principle?) And *how*? (by being introduced to any of the above for the first time? by being challenged to reformulate that which they already know? by apply-ing what they know? by practice? by revision?)

This concentration on intentions does not preclude the possibility that a teacher may, under certain circumstances, take advantage of some unplanned event or unexpected arousal of intense interest and set tasks not congruent with the initial plan. Serendipity of this kind may make the record even more valuable. While we regard the problems explored in this chapter as important considerations when devising a useful and comprehensive record of work done, the status of the schemata is illustrative, not prescriptive. In concluding this section we will attempt to incorporate the lessons we have learned in a single comprehensive record of work done, so that its value and feasibility may be judged.

Consider again the lesson task on 'How submarines work' which was one of the tasks completed by pupils studying the topic 'Water' (see p. 218). In this task it would be possible to identify components which correspond to what we have called cognitive levels:

Procedures. The experimental, how to sink and raise the squeezy bottle using expired air blown down the rubber tube.

Facts. Observed facts such as the behaviour of the squeezy bottle under different conditions; terminology, e.g. ballast tank, hydroplane, compressed air.

Skills. Using observation, interpreting observations. Design of investigation. Performing investigations. (These are APU (Science) categories.) Writing descriptive account of procedure and of explanation.

Concepts. Gas, compression, density, flotation and pumping.

Principles. A solid object will rise to the surface of a liquid in which it is immersed providing its density is less than that of the liquid.

The Bennett–Desforges dimension of the record which includes such categories as 'incremental tasks', 'restructuring tasks', 'enrich-ment tasks', etc., requires a knowledge of each pupil's 'educational' history. These workers have found from their studies of matching that some teachers, though not all, can accurately match tasks to pupils. It is therefore at least potentially possible for each individual pupil involved in the 'submarine' task to locate the cognitive level of demand in one of these categories. For example, John White's record is given in Table 8.5.

To sum up, then, this chapter has argued that record-keeping

Topic: Water
Task: How submarines work
Name: John White

Cognitive 'level'	Accretion	Restructuring	Enrichment	Practice	Revision
Procedures: Experimental					
Facts: observed, floating and sinking air and water	×				
terminology, especially ballast, hydroplane, compressed air	×				
Skills: using observation	×				
interpreting observation		×			
designing investigation			×		
performing investigation	×	×			
describing experiment		×			
writing explanation			×		
Concepts: gas	×	×			
compression	×	×			
density/mass, volume	×	×			
pumping		×			
Principles: Flotation	×	×			

Note that *all* pupils in John White's working group would receive entries in the same rows. The *column* location of each tick might be different for each pupil.

which explores the intellectual demands of a task and the fulfilment of that demand is both conspicuously lacking and absolutely essential in primary (and indeed secondary) education. We have tentatively explored some possible approaches to such task analysis. To be able to carry out such procedures is a prerequisite of effective record-keeping; and it is to this subject that we turn for our final chapter.

9

The Assessment of Achievement

In the previous chapter we began the difficult process of trying to analyse tasks in order to identify within them their intellectual demands. We did this with a view to trying to be able to assess, for any given pupil, whether he or she is making progress during topic lessons, and to examine in more detail than is common something of the nature of that progress. In this chapter the theme is pursued, with the emphasis on the actual keeping of records by the teacher, and also with an eye on the practicalities of time constraints, so it is suggested as we proceed that selective or sampling methods of assessing the overall progress of the class might be feasible.

Being exposed to learning experiences is one thing, benefiting from them is another. However precise and well-organised descriptions of 'tasks' undertaken are, descriptions of how pupils responded to them are essential if a teacher receiving new pupils is to function effectively. It is convenient to consider these responses in two broad categories, cognitive achievement and affective responses. In the first we include such substantive intellectual gains as knowledge acquired, concepts developed and the growth of abilities requisite for the conceptual organisation of knowledge and its application in such activities as problem-solving. The second, equally significant, includes the attitudes of pupils towards particular curricular elements, whether they be identified by their content or the nature of demands made on pupils. Children develop learned dispositions towards mathematics or fractions, towards language work or undirected 'free response' writing, which teachers may disregard to the disadvantage of their pupils.

It is interesting in this context to examine the kinds of record kept by Infant and Junior schools as reported in the Schools Council Survey, and particularly to consider how 'achievement' is

239

Table 9.1: Proportion of sample schools including curriculum categories in records (n = 192)

Skill/curriculum category	% of schools
1. Reading development	96
2. List of mathematical topics covered	81
3. Social/personal development	55
4. Writing development	35
5. Oral language development	34
6. Physical development	31
7. Concept attainment in mathematics	29
8. Scientific skills and experience	17
9. Aesthetic development — craft skills	14
10. Study skills	3

Source: P. Clift, *Record keeping in the primary school*, Schools Council Research Studies (Macmillan, Basingstoke, 1981).

represented in these records. The table above was given in the report (Table 9.1).

Not surprisingly, reading and mathematics are the curriculum categories most often the subject of records. It is remarkable how infrequently other aspects of the curriculum are represented, and particularly striking is the almost complete absence of records of achievement which may uniquely stem from topic work, or any study of those forms of knowledge which occupy a substantial part of the secondary schools' curriculum, for example physics or history.

Of more than passing interest is the use of the term 'development', which occurs in six entries out of the ten recorded here. The term 'development' implies the *natural* progressive manifestation of latent talent which under appropriate environmental conditions will inevitably occur. In the case of physical development, which presumably comprises such factors as height, weight, shape, as well as motor co-ordination, agility and muscle power, the existence of genetic factors is well established, and some environmental factors which affect the expression of the genes involved are known, for example diet. Of these 192 schools, 31 per cent keep records of physical development. Do they suppose that schools have a major influence on physical development? Is such an assumption justified? Given a record of physical development, what action can/do schoolteachers take to provide an environment more propitious for the development of the inherited potentials of pupils (compare Piaget's descriptive theory of cognitive development)?

Similarly, in the case of 'social and personal development', while it is more likely to be environmentally than genetically determined, the influence of school, if it is a day-school, is unlikely to be as powerful as the influence of home and neighbourhood. However there is evidence (Rutter *et al*. 1979) that schools *do* make a difference to the behaviour of *some* pupils in respect of absenteeism and delinquency. There is also evidence to suggest that pupils' *attitude to school*, their behaviour *in* school and their *self-image* can be seriously influenced by their experience while in school. The question remains, what aspects of pupils' social and personal development are recorded? And what effects do such records have on the teacher audience who reads them?

On the other hand reading development may, for the majority of children (we suspect), be largely influenced by environmental factors, many of which operate in schools. Making explicit the use of words, combining words into sentences, and combining these into paragraphs of prose to convey and receive meaning are more likely to occur in schools that at home. The abilities of the pupil to transmit and receive thoughts and feelings by means of the written word are legitimate behaviours for the teacher's attention, observation and description. Here the problem is that of finding ways to identify and describe the present competences of a pupil so that appropriate action may be taken both to capitalise on them and to advance them. Describing facts, articulating ideas and speculations, giving instructions, putting feelings into words, are among the competences which, each with regard to intended audiences, are the marks of a competent writer. The converse of this is to understand and appreciate the written word. It is unlikely that the calculation of a mere 'reading age' will validly represent the diversity of meanings required by teachers upon which they can act in the best interests of the pupils they receive.

Finally, it is worth reflecting on the differences between entry No. 2 in Table 9.1, 'list of mathematical topics covered' (81 per cent), and entry No. 7, 'concept attainment in mathematics' (29 per cent). The former is a description of topics, i.e. curriculum *content* to which pupils have been *exposed*; the latter describes 'concepts' which should indicate the organising principles which, with the power of generalisability and economy of thought, give meaning to superficially different phenomena. Ideally the latter describe achievements, not only exposure. As we will see later, it is deceptively easy to compare pupils, that is, to discriminate between them by 'global' tests which purport to encapsulate in a single measure a

Figure 9.1: Record-keeping

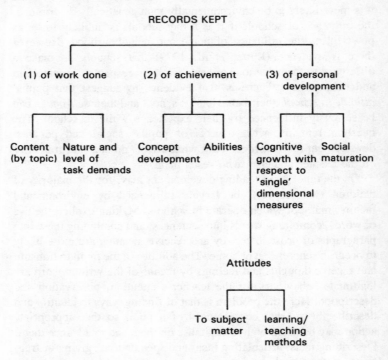

range of competencies, but much more difficult to attempt to describe 'stages' in the development of a concept.

On the basis of these considerations, and other issues discussed in the Clift report and in our own surveys and case studies of teachers at work, we have tried to map the essential features of record-keeping and assessment principles and practice.

Figure 9.1 illustrates one way of classifying records by their content. Each category may be examined, its validity assessed, and the use to which data contained in it might be put may be scrutinised by an appropriate audience.

Whereas the previous chapter was concerned with records of *work done* this final chapter focuses on *achievement* in terms of intellectual growth and the development of positive attitudes towards what is learnt, how it is learnt and the conditions in which it is learnt. We have deliberately restricted our discussion of assessing achievement to those aspects which we believe to be mainly under the influence of the school and which are potentially most useful to teachers.

In the case of cognitive achievement such as mathematical competence, it may, in some cases, be sufficient for a teacher to know a pupil's percentile rank, with respect to the population of, say, eleven-year-old pupils on some standardised test. Indeed many secondary schools apply such tests to their intakes. However, while such procedures might be appropriate for screening and streaming purposes, the information available, a norm-referenced score, does not provide sufficient information on which to base such curriculum decisions as what to teach, at what level, approached in what way.

More information might be gained if the test consisted of items designed according to some clearly defined set of specifications such that the conceptual and skill demands of each were known. Then we could investigate, for each pupil, the pattern of that pupil's responses to sets of items or individual items. If we are concerned in a general way to know that with respect to what the test measures pupil A is better than pupil B, then standardised tests are adequate. If, however, we wish to know what pupils A and B can do with respect to some defined curriculum then standardised tests are inadequate. Teachers can only achieve an appropriate match between their pupils' competence and the tasks they set and their teaching strategies and tactics when they receive more detailed information than typical standardised tests allow.

An alternative method of reporting achievement which has been widely considered in recent years is criterion-referenced (rather than norm-referenced) testing. In such 'measures' of achievement, with respect to a particular competence or other educational outcome of exposure to a curriculum, a criterion of performance is defined and described in operational terms. A test item (or task) or series of items (or tasks) is then devised which requires for its correct 'solution' the competence under scrutiny at the level required by the criterion. Pupils, by demonstrating that they can/cannot successfully engage in the item (or task) are presumed to have achieved/not achieved the criterion. This procedure for assessing attainment is not without difficulties. Observation of a pupil's performance on a criterion-referenced item (or task), or a number of such items, leads to inferences about the pupils' current cognitive state and to predictions about his future performance. While norm-referenced tests have been criticised for the lack of pedagogically useful information they yield, well-designed tests are at least reliable, in so far as different versions of the same test will rank the same set of pupils in the same or very similar order. On the other hand, criterion-referenced tasks (or test items) yield a potentially vast amount of information, but their reliability is questionable if a single or a few tasks (or items) are used to allow pupils an opportunity to exhibit a particular criterial behaviour. This problem is closely related to information-load and to the tension between specific information about a pupil's performance on a particular task, which might inform the teacher how to intervene tactically, and generalisable inferences about a pupil's cognitive development. It is of interest to note that the Assessment of Performance (Science) Unit, when reporting their results (1982), chose in some cases to sum scores across items (but within categories of items each designed to make the same demand) and in other cases to report results on *individual* items.

We now turn to the difficult question of summarising, collecting and organising records of pupils' cognitive achievements. This is followed by a separate consideration of probing pupils' concepts, and finally of the problems of acquiring evidence of and recording pupils' affective states.

In the previous chapter, which dealt with records of *work done*, an attempt was made to specify for each *task* the level at which pupils were required to function. These levels were believed to represent degrees of complexity or difficulty or generality, power and economy in dealing with experience. At the lowest level were facts, each of which might be retained as a specific bit of information unconnected with any other bit of information; at the highest level were general principles, which in a sense not only apprehend large numbers of facts but explain the relationships between facts in ways which allow facts to be explained or as yet unknown facts to be predicted.

One way of recording achievement may thus stem directly from the previous record of tasks set. Successful engagement by a pupil in set (and classified) tasks could be recorded. By duplicating the grids (see Table 9.2) for all tasks and all pupils, a record of achievement, i.e. success or otherwise in these engagements, could be made.

To keep such a record seems a tall order, so it may be that some teachers would prefer the kind of 'summary' of achievement as might be obtained, not by intermittent or continuous assessment, but by testing. In order to find out if the pupil has learnt what the teacher intended such a test would be made up of items or questions (or tasks) which made demands consistent with those typically made in the learning tasks. One or two items in the test (more if time allowed) would represent classes of demands made in topic tasks. A problem associated with this way of proceeding is that it may lead to the award of marks or grades by which normative comparisons might be made. Test which discriminate between pupils may serve the function of sorting pupils into sets, each of which are assigned to different treatments. Knowledge of such marks and grades could serve to motivate pupils. However, it is inevitable that information about what a pupil has achieved will be lost because the test can only be a sample of tasks (as items) which represent *all* tasks of the types (represented in the test) which were present in the topic. As with all sampling, this may lead to random error which may mislead by over- or under-estimating the real achievement of a pupil. Moreover the publication of marks or grades, while providing healthy motivation for one pupil, could lead to a scramble for extrinsic rewards in others.

The major problem is, however, how to devise the means of *summarising* information about achievement but still produce a record which accurately represents what the pupil has demonstrated his/her ability to do (under defined conditions). It is not a question of 'Is Janet better than John at x?' but of 'Can Janet and John do x?' where x is that which we have tried to teach them.

One well-known attempt to summarise achievements in classes arranged hierarchically was made by Benjamin B. Bloom *et al.* in his chapter on 'The cognitive domain' in *Taxonomy of educational objectives* (1956). Bloom invented six classes of objectives, each including a set of cognitive behaviours, as follows: knowledge, comprehension, application, analysis, synthesis and evaluation.

Such a list would be an alternative to the cognitive dimension in Figure 9.2, with which it shares some characteristics. Each of Bloom's categories represents an ability to do x where x is a set of behaviours. Thus *knowledge* is the title given to the set of behaviours all identified by the response to the demands to recall (remember) specific facts, terms, conventions, trends, classifications (both categories and criteria), methods, principles, gereralisations, theories and structures. Recalling these bits of information is the only requirement in this set; pupils are not called upon to demonstrate their understanding of these facts or their ability to apply them.

Information or knowledge is recognised as an important outcome of education. Few topics which we have seen taught and heard described did not contain a substantial load of information. We presume that teachers expected pupils to learn and retain at least a core of salient knowledge as a result of exposure to these topics. Items of such knowledge could be listed, evidence that a pupil has learnt and remembered this knowledge be obtained and recorded.

As we move from the knowledge category to those categories 'above' knowledge a new factor is introduced. To know x is distinct from being able to use x. Bloom relates 'intellectual skills', 'knowledge' and 'abilities' as follows:

skills + knowledge = abilities

He describes skills as 'modes of operation and generalised techniques for dealing with problems'. A 'pure' test of a skill would require 'little or no specialised or technical information'; 'whatever information is required is assumed to be part of the general fund of knowledge'.

In conversation with a group of teachers involved in the present study, about topic work and its likely benefits to pupils, the case-study worker noted the following references to skills:

Accessing skills. Knowing how to use a library, an index, to skim a page of print to locate information.

Comprehension skills. Skimming, looking for main points, reading 'between the lines', detecting bias in accounts.

Observation skills. Matching accurately, being able to describe what is seen.

Recording skills. Note-taking, tabulating and drawing graphs.

Such skills seem to be fairly consistent with Bloom's description. Bloom distinguishes between skills and abilities by reference to the combination of knowledge and skills which characterises the latter. He states 'in solving problems requiring intellectual *abilities* the student is expected to organise or reorganise a problem, to remember such material, and make use of it in the problem situation.'

SOME 'ABILITIES' EXAMINED

The first *abilities* category in Bloom's list is 'comprehension'. This is a large class which he divides into three: 'translation', 'interpretation' and 'extrapolation'. The data upon which the comprehending mind acts may be concrete: things seen, heard or felt, or iconic as graphs, or symbolic in the form of words, numbers, sentences, equations. Bloom restricts this comprehension category to 'an understanding of the literal meaning', higher categories are used for the 'fullest grasp of a message'.

The sub-category 'translation', includes not only the simplest acts of 'comprehension' by which a pupil by a one-to-one comparison changes each element in a communication from one 'language into another', but also such tasks as 'state the problem *in your own words*' and writing a précis.

This category merges into the next sub-category, called 'interpretation'. Acts in this category all require that the major ideas in a passage (or array of data) are understood and their interrelationships are identified. Recognising inconsistencies in arguments or the 'limits within which interpretations can be drawn' are features of this level of comprehension.

The third category, 'extrapolation', requires that the reader (or explorers of the data) can go beyond the message presented by the author to examine its implications, to recognise the consequences of arguments or trends beyond those identified by the author.

After 'knowledge' and 'comprehension' the next major category is 'application'. Bloom differentiates between comprehension and application by reference to problem-solving. Whereas in the former the pupil is required to demonstrate 'the use of an abstraction when its use is specified', in the latter the pupil must determine which abstractions to use in order to attempt to solve a problem. Put simply, 'comprehension' means demonstrating that a 'message' has been understood, 'application' means using the ideas (principles, concepts) in other contexts.

Bloom illustrates this diagrammatically, as shown in Figure 9.2.

These three categories, 'knowledge', 'comprehension' and 'application', are the 'lower' members of this hierarchical system of six categories. The remaining categories are 'analysis', 'synthesis' and 'evaluation'.

While it may be desirable for some purpose to use all these categories and their subdivisions, an initial attempt to record the knowledge acquired and abilities achieved in topic work, at primary stage, may not benefit from too sophisticated a scheme. Moreover the cut-off point between one category and the next is in some cases rather arbitrary. Thus only one further category will be described, that of 'synthesis'. This set of abilities includes all those by which a 'unique' communication or a plan (or set of operations) is produced,

Figure 9.2: Problem-solving

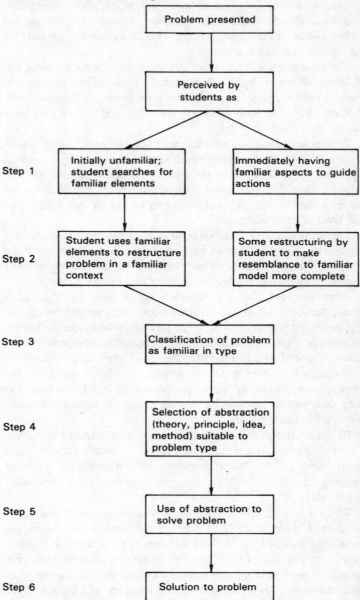

Source: B.S. Bloom *et al.*, *Taxonomy of educational objectives* (Longman, London, 1956), p. 121.

or where a new relationship between two or more ideas is articulated. Here 'unique' means unique for the pupil (Bloom *et al.*, 1956, pp. 169–72).

Production of a unique communication
— Illustrative educational objectives

Skill in writing, using an organisation of ideas and statements.

Ability to write creatively a story, essay or verse for personal pleasure, or for the entertainment or information of others.

Ability to tell a personal experience effectively.

Ability to make extemporaneous speeches.

Ability to write simple musical compositions, as in setting a short poem to music.

Production of a plan, or proposed set of operations
— Illustrative educational objectives

Ability to propose ways of testing hypotheses.

Ability to integrate the results of an investigation into an effective plan or solution to solve a problem.

Ability to plan a unit of instruction for a particular teaching situation.

Ability to design simple machine tools to perform specified operations.

Ability to design a building according to given specifications.

Derivation of a set of abstract relations
— Illustrative educational objectives

Ability to formulate appropriate hypotheses based upon an analysis of factors involved, and to modify such hypotheses in the light of new factors and considerations.

Ability to formulate a theory of learning applicable to classroom teaching.

Ability to perceive various possible ways in which experience may be organised to form a conceptual structure.

Ability to make mathematical discoveries and generalisations.

Table 9.2: Record of achievement

Topic: Roads *Cognitive category*	Task I	II	III	etc.
Knowledge	×			
Comprehension	×			
Translation	×			
Interpretation				
Extrapolation				
Application				
Synthesis				

Using Bloom to categorise tasks

Task I

If we refer back to the three tasks set during the 'Roads' topic which were discussed in chapter 8, it is possible to see how such tasks might be converted into a record of achievement made according to a reduced version of Bloom's scheme, as in Table 9.2.

Task 1 required pupils to find out from library sources 'all you can about modern road-building'. Questions directed them to specific facts, for example, Which people are involved? What machinery do they use? Presumably the teacher who set this work had some expectations about the facts pupils would acquire from books. If he had decided on a set of the more significant facts which he expected pupils to learn he could have determined *some time later* if this particular educational objective had been achieved by his pupils. In this case 'knowledge' is apparently an objective. However, we may infer from the instruction to 'write about all the different stages' and 'draw pictures to illustrate your work' that the objective of 'comprehension' at some level is involved. Such an inference depends on the assumption that the teacher would not accept pupils merely copying chunks of text but would require them to put into their own words the information they had read. It is doubtful if such textual material as might be available would rise above 'translation'. Note however that a knowledge of both the text and the pupils' written response would be necessary before a judgement could be made on

(a) whether the pupil had achieved comprehension, and
(b) at what level this was achieved.

Task I therefore might have resulted in the achievement of 'knowledge' and 'comprehension' objectives. To know if the former had been achieved it would be necessary to specify the facts to be learnt and to arrange some form of testing. Achievement of the latter would be ascertainable by reference to the pupils' written response to the task.

Task II

Task II required pupils to use a 'mileage chart' to determine the distances between specified towns and calculate the time taken to travel from A to B at a given speed. Thus pupils were required to *know* and *use* the procedures for finding the distances between towns. Presumably one of the teacher's expectations was that on a future occasion pupils would remember this procedure. The demand to do this at some future time would be classified in Bloom's knowledge-of-procedures category. The *use* of this system implies some effort of comprehension, admittedly at a low level. Possibly 'comprehension–translation' is an appropriate classification for this task.

The next step which the pupils are required to take was the calculation of time taken to travel a given distance when speed is known (and assumed to be average or constant — an assumption not made explicit in the task set). These are problems which require the pupils to *comprehend* the relationship between time, distance and speed *and* to recall the procedures for division. It is reasonable to regard these parts of the task as the application of a mathematical process to the problem set. Reference to Table 9.3 shows that the columns on the right correspond to the mental activities which might be supposed to be used by the pupil when 'solving' such a problem.

Successful completion of this task would therefore be recorded as follows:

Table 9.3: Completion of task

Topic: Roads *Cognitive category*	Task		
	I	II Time Distance Speed	III
Knowledge			
Comprehension			
Translation		×	
Interpretation			
Extrapolation			
Application		×	
Synthesis			

Task III

The third task in its original form (see page 232) seemed to consist initially of a set of instructions which, if followed, produced a set of circles and letters of different colour combinations. If we disregard the effort required to understand the instructions there may not have been much cognitive activity during this phase of the task. However, later, pupils were asked 'to see which sign shows up most clearly' and told to 'vary the distance 25m, 50m and 100m'. Even at this stage the task is a set of instructions to be followed rather than a problem to be solved. Clearly there is a problem: which combination of colours is visible from the greatest distance? It may be that in addition to the task set on the work-card this had been discussed in experimental terms, for example, pupils might have been asked how each pair of colours could be given a 'fair' test. Had pupils tried to design such an experiment they would have been functioning at high cognitive levels, demanding at least 'application' and possibly 'synthesis'. However, classification of the demand made during this task given on the card is difficult, because the cognitive demand seems to have been light. Possibly the measuring of the distance between card and observer is an elementary case of *application*, and so this task may be recorded, 'Task III (signs): measurement — application'.

252

A POSSIBLE SYSTEM FOR RECORDING ACHIEVEMENT

In order to explore the feasibility of producing a record based on this restricted version of Bloom's categories, ten tasks given to a third-year junior class during the topic 'Roads' in our case study were examined in order to determine the significant educational objectives (cognitive), the achievement of which would be displayed if correct/acceptable responses were made. An appropriate title was given to each task a an *aide-mémoire*, and a cross was made in each 'cell' in the column that indicates the level of significant demand made by each task (Figure 9.3)

A copy of this grid should be made for each pupil engaged on the topic. When a pupil successfully completes a task a tick is placed in the appropriate cell alongside the cross. In the case of knowledge objectives one could use as evidence the short-term recall of a list of important facts. This might be obtained by simply questioning the pupils at the time the task is completed. Longer-term recall might be observed by an end-of-topic test. In all other cases, comprehension, application and synthesis might best be observed during the time the pupil is engaged on the task.

The main difficulty with this system is that of determining the criteria by which a successful performance is judged. When teachers devise tasks for pupils they have in mind expectations of how pupils in their class will respond. This same professional judgement should be used in order to determine the criteria of pupils' performance. If, for example, pupils have been gathering information from books (for example about modern road-building, Roman roads, highwaymen or roads in the Middle Ages), provided they have written in their own words a comprehensive account of the more significant points, it may be accepted that they have achieved comprehension of the texts to which they referred. Attention need not be paid to errors of spelling, syntax or punctuation when making the judgement unless they are so gross as to interfere with the central question, 'has the pupil understood the text?' (Of course there will be other tasks set at other times when these matters will be critically important.) Moreover, the teacher may wish to take remedial action even in this case. The central judgement about the pupils' ability to comprehend should not be contaminated by extraneous considerations.

More difficult decisions may have to be made in the synthesis category. A task included in the 'Roads' topic (not listed above) was to 'write about the street which you live in'. This stimulus gave rise

Table 9.4: Summary of records
Topic: Roads

Cognitive category	I Road-building	II Time Distance Speed	III Visibility Signs	IV Highway Code	V Road design	VI* Traffic lights	VII Road-builders	VIII High-waymen	IX Roman roads	X Medieval roads
Knowledge	×								×	×
Comprehension				×			×	×		
Translation		×		×			×	×	×	×
Interpretation										
Extrapolation										
Application		×	×			×				
Synthesis					×					

*Electric circuits; three bulbs to light in correct sequence.

to a variety of responses: some pupils wrote descriptive, rather matter-of-fact accounts, others wrote expressively, still others inventively about alley-cats and learner-drivers. Part of the problem here may have been lack of explicitness by the teacher about his expectations: what sort of an 'account' was it to be? The lesson to be learnt in the interests of accurate records of pupils' achievements is that explicitness in task demand is prerequisite. In this case the teacher would have to decide on his expectations of an adequate response (or set of responses) and tick the synthesis box in those cases where these conditions were met.

Despite these difficulties this system of recording achievement has two virtues. Firstly, the pattern of cognitive demands, within and between topics, is made plain; secondly, the manifest abilities of pupils in relation to topic and time are on record.

CONCEPT DEVELOPMENT: DIAGNOSIS AND GETTING TO GRIPS WITH THE SENSE CHILDREN MAKE OUT OF EXPERIENCE

Background and example

One of the most difficult aspects of achievement to observe and record, and yet by far the most useful and important to the teacher, is the ability of the pupil to make sense of experience. We all form images or constructs in our minds which have evolved from the interplay between experience and the mechanism which our minds have to select and relate data and ideas. Teachers as well as pupils have formed constructs in order to make experience intelligible. The teacher's constructs cannot be imposed on the pupil. The pupils' ability to benefit from experience is determined by their capacity to build and modify *their* constructs. Effective teaching therefore requires of the teacher a willingness and an ability to investigate pupils' responses to experience in order to infer the construct-building processes in their minds and the constructs they are currently using. The Bennett classification uses the term 'restructuring' to achieve some recognition of these processes. Whenever we learn a new fact or are introduced to a new principle, and the new element does not fit our existing constructs, these will have to be modified to accommodate the new element, or the new element will remain incomprehensible.

One of the major shortcomings of recording achievement on the lines suggested by Bloom, in terms of abilities, is the tendency to think of them as properties of mind independent of the particular contexts in which people are called upon to act. Despite Bloom's attempt to include knowledge into his equation 'knowledge + skills = abilities', we still tend to think of, say, 'comprehension' or 'application' as generalisable. When we talk of comprehension tests we imply that the ability 'to comprehend' is independent of content. In the same way, we may fall into the trap of regarding any ability defined in terms of certain kinds of behaviour as a dimension which with other dimensions determines the efficiency of a learner in dealing with new experiences. At best this is only partly true, because this model of the mind fails to take into account the learners' previous experience of particular content and the constructs they have invented to make sense of it.

The problem is to find some practical method of probing the minds of pupils in order to investigate how their responses to topic-work experiences are determined by the constructs which they have in their minds, to find out if and how these change in response to these experiences.

During the case-study work associated with this project selected pupils were subjected to short 'clinical' interviews about the work they were engaged in on their current topics and their responses to them.

A second-year junior class during a half-term topic on 'Water' had done some work on submarines, including some practical work with a 'squeezy' bottle. There follows a transcript of part of a conversation with Andrew (p. 257).

Many teachers who have read this script, or heard the tape from which it was taken, are satisfied with Andrew's grasp of the problem. Within his own terms, and taking into account his age and likely experience, his account is judged to be at least satisfactory. While agreeing with this judgement, there are two features of this conversation which may indicate unresolved problems in Andrew's mind which, if identified, would assist his future learning.

The first relates to the presence of air in the submarine and the conditions under which it floats or sinks. He states at one point that if there is a supply of air in the submarine (sufficient to expel the water from the ballast tanks) it 'would keep them afloat'. This problem appears to be resolved later in the interview by reference to a supply of 'compressed air in a little tank', but it would be worth exploring Andrew's ideas about density and the conditions required for floating and sinking. Why, for example, does he specify a *little* tank?

The second problem is that of his idea about the possible change of weight (mass) of air when compressed. Andrew's construct of air allows it to change weight (mass) under different states of compression. Mass is not conserved in gases under compression. Later Andrew may be obliged to adapt his construct to accommodate new experiences. A look at the transcript illuminates the problem:

ANDREW

CSW. Tell me now, without looking at this, how does a submarine work?

AT. Well, well there's this big tanks at the bottom of the submarine and if the submarine captain wants to make the submarine go down he fills up the tanks, the big tanks, with water, so it'll sink.

CSW. I see, yes.

AT. But, and when he wants to come up, he fills them up with air.

CSW. How does he get rid of the water that's in the tanks?

AT. He gets these big pumps and pumps it out.

CSW. Mmm. I see.

AT. And pumps the air in. And then sometimes he has to keep changing it. I mean, the ballast tanks, the water, because they eat up all the food and use the fuel up, so it changes the weight.

CSW. I see. Oh, you mean, the weight of the submarine changes?

AT. Yes.

CSW. I see. And if it changes they have to adjust the ballast. I've got you, yes. I wonder where they get the air from? I mean, if they're down at the bottom of the sea with their ballast tanks full of water, and they've got to pump air into the . . .

AT. The air would make the submarine come up.

CSW. It's a bit difficult, isn't it? They must carry some air with them, mustn't they?

AT. Yeah, but that would keep them afloat, wouldn't it?

CSW. Mmm. Now, I wonder how they manage to keep a supply of air inside the submarine, so that when they want to get the water out the ballast tanks they can blow air into the ballast tanks?

AT. . . . they'll have to carry air with them.

CSW. Mmm. But as you say, if they carry air why doesn't it keep them afloat? Now that's a bit of a mystery, isn't it?

AT. Yes.

CSW. Have you any ideas as to how they do carry the air?

AT. No.

CSW. Have you ever heard of, er, . . .

AT. Could have compressed air in a little tank.

CSW. Good lad. Yeah, well that's what they'll do, won't they, they'll carry compressed air. If you take a lot of air and compress it, er, will it weigh more, when you compress it?

AT. Weigh the same about.

CSW. Weigh the same. If I took all the air that's in this room now . . .

AT. Yes.

CSW. . . . compress it so that it went into a matchbox, would the air weigh as much or more when it's in the matchbox?

AT. Not quite as much really.

CSW. Not quite as much you don't think.

AT. No. 'Cos it'd all get squashed up.

CSW. All get squashed up would it? Mmm. Good . . . Okey-doke, well, that was your submarine tale, and then after that you went on to floating and sinking. And what did you do there?

At first sight it would seem that to engage pupils in 'clinical' interviews of this kind is logistically impossible for class teachers. This may be true, but the pay-off is potentially so important that it is worth trying to undertake investigations of this type *from time to time with at least some pupils*. We found that playing such interview tapes to the pupils' teacher profoundly affected her perception of her pupils' achievements and the effects of her teaching.

A further example

Consider the following extracts from an interview with Joanne.

JOANNE: *Extract 1*

CSW. Now tell me a bit about your work on how a submarine works. Can you tell me how a submarine works? It's actually how it goes up and down in the sea, that was what it was really about, wasn't it? How does it work then?

JT. Well, it has like weights which are really called ballasts, ballats . . .

CSW. Ballasts, yes.

JT. And, er, when they want to go down they, they, er, put them in and when they want to go up they take them out.

258

CSW. I see. And what sort of weights do they use?

JT. Er, well they're like big sacks. Well cargo.

CSW. I see. Let's say, we had an, er, Fairy liquid container.

JT. Yes.

CSW. And you took all the Fairy liquid out. What would the Fairy liquid container contain, what would be in it?

JT. Air.

CSW. There would be air. And so if you wanted the Fairy liquid container to sink how would you make it sink?

JT. Put water in it and put the top lid back on so no air could get in.

CSW. Right. And it would sink.

JT. The water would pull it down.

CSW. And if you wanted to, er, get the Fairy liquid container back to the surface again, how would you manage that?

JT. Take all the water out and fill it up.

CSW. Mmm. How would you get the water out? There's lots of ways of doing this.

JT. Well, you put a like tube in, in a hole, and blow out the water through the top, and then it will throw it to the top.

CSW. Good, good. You blow the water out of the container. 'Cos that would be the easiest form of ballasting in, wouldn't it? And in fact submarines do use water . . . It would be easiest for them just to open their tanks and let the water and the air out, so they can sink. OK.

The first part of the conversation about submarines yields the inference that Joanne is confused about the term 'ballast' and about the use of water as ballast. She associates ballast with weight but confuses the term with cargo, which has weight but also some other purpose. Yet when required to visualise and explain the principle of floating and sinking of a Fairy liquid container — a concrete example which she has seen — Joanne does much better. However, even here there are signs that her 'construct' of sinking requires further investigation. What does Joanne mean when she describes water as 'pulling [the water-filled bottle] down'?

JOANNE: *Extract 2 (already quoted in chapter 3)*

CSW. I've noticed this heading on 'The Water Cycle'. Could you tell me a bit about the water cycle? What does it mean?

JT. Well, water cycle means that, when the rain comes down, then the sun comes out, then the rain goes back up and into the clouds. The clouds go across, and they come down, and it keeps going *on like that.*

CSW. Oh, I see. So, let's be clear about it; you say the rain comes down from the clouds into the earth. Then what happens?

JT. The water goes back up.

CSW. How does the water go back up? You said the rain *went back up, but you didn't really mean that, did you?*

JT. Well, they form like puddles and the sun sort of, like sucks them up.

CSW. How does it manage to do that?

JT. It shines down and it . . . well, it pulls it up and forms like a cloud.

CSW. There are puddles of water outside this morning. There's one over there out of the window. Can you see that? What will happen to that puddle today? The sun's shining on it: where will it go?

JT. Into the air.

CSW. I wonder how it goes up into the air. Strange isn't it? It's perfectly ordinary water, and we come back this afternoon and it might have disappeared! You've told me it would have gone up into the sky, back into the clouds, is that right? I wonder how we know? How could we get the water out of air? Is there water in the air? I mean, if the water is on its way from that puddle back up into the clouds, then it must be in the air, mustn't it? Do you think so?

JT. Well, sort of, certain parts of water go into the air.

CSW. I see. Watch me breathe on the window. What's happened?

JT. There's condensation.

CSW. . . . Now what is it that's condensed on the window?

JT. Hot air.

CSW. Well it was certainly my hot breath . . . water . . . now it's disappearing . . . where is it going?

JT. Into the air.

The water cycle is difficult for pupils to understand because it involves abstract ideas which cannot be directly observed. When a pool of water 'dries up', i.e. disappears, this may be 'explained' by the hypothesis that 'particles of water have continually escaped from its surface into the air'. Terms such as 'water vapour' and 'evaporation' do not explain how the water disappears, they are merely terms used to describe the hypothesis. The relationship between water vapour and steam and water vapour and clouds as normally 'explained' requires this abstract vapour link, which must be extremely difficult for the young mind to grasp.

Joanne uses phrases which give indications of her difficulty in fitting 'facts' about the water cycle into her conceptual framework (constructs), namely, 'The water goes back up', 'the sun sort of, like, sucks [water] up' and 'certain parts of water go into the air'. Moreover, although she knew the term 'condensation' and used it correctly she nevertheless described the water deposit on the cold window as 'hot air'.

The value of clinical interviews of this type is that the teacher learns how the pupils are dealing with experience. To know this is a prerequisite step for the effective management of a pupil's future learning.

It is accepted that this type of interview cannot be conducted with all pupils at all points in a topic. One reasonable restriction would be to concentrate on one or two tasks which involved key concepts, another would be to 'interview' only those pupils whom you had reasons to believe were in difficulty. The latter implies some rough screening based on normal classroom transactions.

The main problem to be overcome when these logistical decisions have been made is to acquire the investigative skills of the interviewer. Enquiring into a pupil's thinking is not the same as teaching in the conventional sense. Teachers when interviewing must resist the temptation to 'correct' what they may regard as 'errors'. The pupil will in most cases possess constructs. An investigation of these requires probing the meanings of these constructs in terms of their elements, relationships and associations. For example, to have told Joanne that all the water goes into the air, or that water condensed on the window was not hot air, is inappropriate (and could be counter-productive) in an investigation of how Joanne's mind is dealing with these phenomena. Keeping a record of such interviews can probably best be done by preparing notes. Tape recording the interview is some safeguard against inaccurate or premature judgement, but such data have to be reduced to a report or record of key facts and inferences based on these facts.

EXPLORING PUPILS' ATTITUDES

While the pupil as learner has been central to most of what has been said so far, the learner's attitudes to what is being learned have not as yet detained us. Nevertheless, these attitudes are clearly critical. Perhaps educators pay them too little attention simply because, once in the classroom, we monitor them intuitively. However, a more systematic approach is sometimes desirable, and is suggested below.

Before tackling this you may find it helpful to carry out the following suggested activities in your own topic lessons:

1. Ask *yourself* how your pupils feel about the work they cover in topic lessons. Can you identify any of your criteria for making intuitive judgements?

2. Discuss the issue with colleagues and see if they believe they are *au fait* with pupil attitudes to learning.

3. Ask some pupils, casually, what they enjoy most, and least. Ask them for their reasons. Ask them further questions using other descriptors, for instance 'exciting–boring'; 'useful–useless'.

4. Does what you discover fit in with your preconceptions? How does it differ? Do you think the pupils were entirely honest with you?

Recording attitudes

In our case studies we found, in our position as reasonably detached observers, that pupils were willing to tell us about their interest in topic work. They told us which topics were, in their opinion, most interesting and which activities in a topic were of most interest to them, and why. It was rare to find total unanimity of opinion. Some pupils found one topic or activity absorbingly interesting, others did not. Occasionally we were surprised by our findings. Andrew, whose explanation of how submarines work attracted our attention and who writes competently in topic work, finds topic work interesting but English boring. One of his classmates likes the science bits of topic work but was bored by work on trees in a copse adjacent to the school.

As primary teachers largely determine the topics to be studied and wholly the types of activity undertaken within a topic, it would seem useful to know the differential responses of pupils to topics and tasks in terms of attitude. If attitude to task is a component in motivation it may be critically important to know the affective responses of pupils.

Obviously information can be gained by simply asking pupils if they are interested in topic or task, and why. Such information will be more or less distorted depending on the frankness of pupils, their wish to please the teacher and their fear of consequences. More direct methods of observing pupils in action and seeing the consequences of their attitudes have much to commend them.

A classification system of educational objectives in the affective domain (i.e. attitudes and values), similar to Bloom's cognitive classification, was produced by Krathwohl *et al.* (1964). In this classification a major category was invented to include the ways in which pupils *responded* to, say, the content of a lesson or a particular learning experience. Here, only this category will be considered, since if it is in this class the link between observed behaviour and attitude is the most direct.

Before observing pupils' responses in order to determine by inference their attitudes towards topic or task, certain preconditions must exist. First of all, the level of distraction must be kept within reasonable bounds. Second, the way the class is managed must be such as to allow the pupil freedom to respond in a variety of ways. This optimum is necessary in order to facilitate responses of different degrees and different kinds. In our case studies most classrooms seemed to be managed in ways not far from this optimum.

The Krathwohl category 'responding' contains three subdivisions: 'acquiescence in responding'; 'willingness to respond'; and 'satisfaction in response'. Strictly and realistically speaking there ought to be a sub-category 'does not respond' or even 'responds inappropriately'. Krathwohl seems not to contemplate this outcome.

A teacher in one of our case-study schools instructed a second-year class working on the topic 'Water' on how to make a small water wheel out of metal foil and use this to lift a small weight by means of a pulley arrangement around the axle. Pupils worked in pairs. One pair did just as they were told, cut a disc, marked off eight radii, cut half-way down radii, bent foil to form paddles, impaled disc at centre on a pencil, wrapped string around axle, tied weight on end, placed water-wheel paddles under remaining tap, saw weight lifted and then recorded what they had done.

A second pair, having made the water wheel, questioned the teacher about the effect of more or larger paddles and greater or lesser weights on the system.

A third pair not only made a second wheel of the same design to make it more efficient but at home that evening made a series of wheels, varying the number and size of blades and the number of wheels, and investigated their lifting capacity with different ratio/volume flows of water.

Clearly the responses of these three pairs of pupils varied. The first did as they were told — they *acquiesced*. The second explored

263

their experience with the teacher, thought about the variables involved and in a limited way exploited this learning experience. Their response was not merely acquiescent but *willing*. The third group went beyond this, they spent further time and thought on the wheel-building–weight-lifting exercise. Next day they shared this experience with their teacher and seven classmates. Here was an illustration of *satisfaction* in response.

In general one may differentiate between these three levels of response, *acquiescence*, *willingness* and *satisfaction*, by reference to the following questions:

1. Is the pupil under observation engaged in a learning task specifically as directed by the teacher?

2. Is the pupil engaged in *task-related* behaviour additional to the specific instructions given by the teacher?

3. Given a choice (or some opportunity), do pupils
    (a) volunteer to work at activity?
    (b) show willingness to continue to work on task when a change of activity is called for if bell goes for break?
    (c) try to engage other pupils in task-related talk?
    (d) use words in relation to task which indicate satisfaction, e.g. 'I've got it', 'great', 'fab', 'neat', 'interesting'?

4. What is the ratio of task-related to non-task-related activity?

Question 1 relates to acquiescence in responding. This sub-category, like others in this class, includes species of 'doing something about the phenomenon besides merely perceiving it'. At this lowest level work is done in a *compliant* way. Pupils do what the teacher tells them to do, no more, no less. The next category beyond acquiescence (revealed by the answer to Question 2) is a *willingness* to respond, which is characterised by pupils entering voluntarily into task-related behaviours to which they have not been specifically directed. Such a class of behaviours includes going on to another task of a kind similar to that assigned by the teacher at one level and exploratory behaviour at a 'higher' level. The pupil is not merely acquiescing, but willingly entering into alternative task-related endeavours.

The answers to questions 3 and 4 indicate a 'higher' level of response than *willingness*. The name given to this sub-class, *satisfaction*, implies that an inference must be made from observations. Satisfaction is a feeling, not a response. However, volunteering, persisting, sharing and reacting with verbal spontaneity in the manner described may be the behavioural manifestations of satisfaction.

Who should be observed? how often? for how long? are questions which can only be answered when the purpose of the record to be made is known. If, for example, we wished to compare pupils' responses to different topics (or kinds of tasks) we might secure sufficient data by selecting a sample of half a dozen pupils and observing them two or three times each lesson for 30 seconds. If, however, we wished to obtain information about the affective response of one or more pupils to all tasks in a topic the system would have to be modified accordingly. For example, we could concentrate on pupils whose attitude to topic work is of particular interest, or simply record cases where pupils respond at the satisfaction level. The effort made by the teacher will be a function of how important it is to her to know about the affective response of pupils to their work.

POSTSCRIPT

The procedures for making records described here are by no means exhaustive. Some well-known systems with great potential usefulness have been omitted. The main criterion for inclusion was that each system exemplified a possible solution to a particular problem. All the systems described here can be elaborated, simplified or adapted to meet the particular requirements of individual schools and their unique circumstances. By exploring a variety of *purposes* which might be served by the systematic collection of data and their storage as records it is hoped that colleagues, if they identify with these purposes, will be persuaded to give the systems a trial in their schools or to devise systems which serve them better. We take the distinctions we have tried to make between records of work done, achievement, concept development and attitudes to be important in the process of communicating with different audiences.

These audiences may be the teacher who made the record, other teachers in the same or another school, parents or the pupils themselves. There is no point in making a record unless an audience has been identified and the use to which the record will be put is known. The teacher as an 'audience' for her own records may be interested in at least three purposes which records can serve. To map out in a reasonably systematic way the cognitive level of tasks given to pupils during the course of a topic *facilitates an overview of the intellectual challenge given to pupils*. References to pupils' personal history of contact with this and similar topics allows more *accurate matching of task* to the known capabilities of particular children.

Records of achievement, in terms of abilities which individual pupils display, or more particularly in terms of conceptual growth, are the means by which teachers may *diagnose pupils' learning strengths or weaknesses and act appropriately*.

A third purpose is the assistance which records of achievement can provide in the *evaluation of the content of a topic and the strategies used to teach it*. Is it at an appropriate conceptual level? Were the demands made on pupils too easy or too hard? Records of pupils' affective response to a topic or the way it was presented or explored would also be helpful in this regard. *Do most pupils exhibit satisfaction in response to the topics set before them*?

An interesting feature of records of tasks, either in terms of the kinds of demands they make or in terms of pupils' achievement, is the way they reflect on the teacher's aims and curriculum plans. For instance, the 'forecast' produced by a teacher for the topic 'Water' (see page 220), in the form of a flow diagram, might have been modified if that teacher had been more aware of some of the conceptual problems associated with floating and sinking or evaporation and condensation. Similarly such 'headings' as 'Transport' would benefit from a consideration of the concepts involved.

Other teachers, or the heads of those schools receiving pupils, will undoubtedly benefit from the more comprehensive records of the tasks which pupils have attempted, their success in the enterprise and their affective response to different topics and tasks within topics, which these suggested schemes facilitate. One would add that while, typically, other teachers may be an audience for this kind of information, much might be gained by teachers actively collaborating in collecting data — particularly by observing and interviewing pupils from another class.

Pupils themselves are an audience for records, especially of achievement and attitudes. A teacher's professional judgement based on the intimate knowledge of individual pupils would determine the circumstances in which selected data would be used. If it can be demonstrated that access to the data — which are explicitly *not* comparative but are descriptive — acts as a spur or gives rise to satisfaction the case is made for communicating them to pupils.

Finally, parents might benefit from descriptions of their children's progress illustrated by reference to data such as those indicated here rather than the often bland platitudes with which they are sometimes fed.

Conclusion

At the beginning of this book we indicated that it was not the intention to set out a prescription of how topic work in schools should be taught. Rather, the aim was to use cases of topics in action, first to raise issues about topic teaching and, second, to illuminate these issues by looking at examples of current practice. We identified, in chapter 3, four major issues: managing the curriculum, preparing to teach a topic, teaching skills and classroom processes in topic work, and record-keeping and assessment. In chapters 4 to 9 these issues have been explored, substantially by drawing upon actual cases from specific schools. Although we intend to remain true to our intention of shunning prescription, there are none the less some general points that can usefully be made about the preconditions for successful topic work. It is these remarks that we have drawn together in this concluding section of the book.

Of all the issues raised throughout the life of the Schools Council project it was that of management which gave us most cause for concern in some of the schools we visited. We concluded that effective management of topic work and its curriculum, at both school and classroom level, was essential to any justification for topic as a way of working. There were specific dimensions to this management issue that could be identified and which were generally prerequisite. First, schools where work was apparently most educationally sound had clearly defined policies for topic work. It was less important whether these had been imposed or whether they had been more democratically negotiated; what was significant was that they existed. A feature of that existence was that they were known, agreed, and acted upon by all staff, and that they were communicated to new staff who joined the school. This statement of policy had to contain a set of clearly defined aims and intentions, and a cluster of stated learning outcomes expected of pupils, so that teachers could refer back to these as a model for their work.

Second, schools where work stood out as distinctive had tended to develop what we called a 'style' of their own. This might mean that they made carefully planned use of the school's specific environment and built on this strength, or it might mean that the teachers had developed a very special relationship with one another to enable them to work as a team so as to use each person's strengths to particular effect. In the case studies reported in this book 'style' is specially noticeable at Roseborough school.

Overall, too, it seemed to us that management issues in schools were best solved where there was consultation between head and staff, and between class teachers and, for example, year-group leaders. Again, it did not matter whether this was achieved through formal or informal mechanisms — but it was crucial. Further, consultation implies planning. All the teachers in our study carried out at least a minimum of classroom planning: most planned with care and professionalism. But the best topic work was found where teachers got together to plan on a wider than 'my classroom/your classroom' basis.

Next, the effective planning and management of topic work implied that thought had been given to the selection of the specific content, skills and concepts pupils were asked to learn at any given stage in their school career. In the Dovecote Mill extracts quoted in this study we have seen something of the content/progression debate in progress; in the Blaydon and Roseborough extracts we have witnessed two more or less sophisticated solutions to the problems.

Finally on the management issue there is the cluster of questions that concern staff development. A (to us) surprising result of the Schools Council project in a number of a studied schools was that, when the next scale post became available, it was allotted to a 'consultant for topic work'. If this was the valid use of a post, then it had to be asked why the step had not been taken before, and why so many schools outside the project did not seem to have pursued this particular management strategy. No doubt our presence as project officers had heightened awareness, and no doubt this was all to the good. Our presence also helped, for a while, to meet another expressed need: for in-service training concerned with topic work in LEAs. This genuinely seemed to be unavailable in many areas, and perhaps some advisory teams need to look to this as a way of supporting teachers.

After management, the next major issue pursued in this book has been that of preparing to teach topics. Here, as we have indicated, we found teachers very articulate and obviously skilled. In fact, the checklist on page 154 makes informative reading, and is a good example of how collected professional wisdom can be used by other professionals and trainee professionals. Little more needs to be said on this subject at this juncture.

The third major issue relates to classroom process and the matter of a teacher's skills. Though the situation in the profession is generally better than it was, we still came to the view that too few teachers have the time or the techniques to effectively analyse dimensions of their performance. Too many classrooms are 'fine and private' places wherein might be cobwebs or treasure beyond price — but few outsiders penetrate to discover. Above all, there seemed to be certain skills that could be identified as key skills for teachers to develop and for in-service work to pick up. Teachers need, perhaps, to give more attention to their rationales for grouping pupils, and to the reasons why they adopt particular teaching/learning styles. Lessons, and nowhere is this more true than of project lessons, need beginnings that pack punch and endings that are coherent. Task setting is a skill that must be refined to a greater degree so that pupils' work is genuinely purposeful. Those same pupils need to develop independence in learning, through study skills but above all through *attitudes*.

Another significant teaching skill is that of questioning; and we have looked at this in some detail in chapter 7. Through a judicious use of question technique and task-setting teachers can move closer to the ideal of all education, which is to meet the needs of pupils as individuals. Finally on this issue, flexibility was a word to which our studied teachers attached importance: certainly the best teachers are those who plan for a variety of outcomes and do not totally precondition the children's learning, and who can think on their feet so as to use the leads and interests of the children.

The fourth major issue that this book has identified is that of assessing what children have learned, and of communicating this information to others in professionally valid and meaningful ways. Chapters 8 and 9 have looked at the techniques. It remains for us to say here that this was an issue that was not tackled at all in many schools, and tackled ineffectively in most others. It is crucial to effective teaching: only when the issue has been resolved can the intentions and end-products of learning be compared, and the progression of children be assured. Only then, too, can a logical curriculum be sustained, and the teacher rest satisfied in the knowledge that he or she can properly account (be it to head, adviser, HMI, parent, ratepayer) for the job done. Not only that, assessment is crucial to effective learning: how else will a child receive the advice necessary to improve his or her performance?

These, then, were some of the messages that we took away from our collection of the case-study material, some of which has been reported and commented on in this book. There were many sub-issues, of course, and many other leads that could have been followed. But part of the purpose in compiling this material was for others to read and to decide what most affects their own situation. If we have been successful you will, by now, have come to your own conclusions.

References

Adelman, C., Jenkins, D., Kemmis, S. (1977) 'Rethinking case-study': notes from the second Cambridge Conference, *Cambridge Journal of Education*, vol. 6, pp. 139–50

Aitken, M., Bennett, N. and Hesketh, J. (1981) 'Teaching styles and pupil progress: a re-analysis', *British Journal of Educational Psychology*, vol. 51.2, pp. 170–86

Alexander, R.J. (1984) *Primary teaching*, Holt, Rinehart and Winston, London

Allen, G. and Collis, M.(1972) 'Integration in the primary school in theory and practice', *School Science Review*, vol. 53, June 1972

Ashley, B., Cohen, H. and Slatter, B. (1967) 'Social classifications: relevance of the teacher', *The Times Educational Supplement*, 17 March

Assessment of Performance Unit (1982) *Science in Schools. Age 13: Report No. 1*, HMSO, London

Atkins, M.J. (1984) 'Practitioner as researcher: some techniques for analysing semi-structured data in small scale research', *British Journal of Educational Studies*, vol. 32.2, pp. 251–61

Barker-Lunn, J. (1984) 'Junior school teachers: their methods and practices', *Educational Research*, vol. 26.3

Bennett, N. *et al.* (1976) *Teaching styles and pupil progress*, Open Books, London

Bennett, N. *et al.* (1980) *Open plan schools: curriculum and design*, NFER, Slough

Bennett, N. and Desforges, C. (1984) *The quality of pupils' learning experiences*, Lawrence Earlbaun, Hillsdale, New Jersey

Bennett, N., O'Hare, E. and Lee, J. (1982) *Mixed age classes in primary schools*, Centre for Educational Research and Development, Lancaster

Berliner, D. and Tikunoff, W. (1976) 'The California beginning teacher evaluation study: overview of the ethnographic study', *Journal of Teacher Education*, vol. 27.1

Bloom, B. *et al.* (1956) *Taxonomy of educational objectives*, Longman, London

Blyth, J. (1984) *Place and time with children aged 5–9*, Croom Helm, London

Blyth, W.A. (1972) *Schools Council Project History/Geography/Social Sciences*, Schools Council Project, Liverpool

Bolwell, L.H. (1973) 'A case for environmental education in schools', *Educational Development*, vol. 13.1

Boydell, D. (1979) 'Classroom groups in theory and practice', *Education 3–13*, vol. 7.2

Brown, G. and Hatton, N. (1982) *Effective explanations*, Macmillan, Basingstoke

Bullock Report (1975) *A language for life*, HMSO, London

Cast, P. (1979) *All the years round*, Local Education Authority, Nottinghamshire

Clift, P. (1981) *Record keeping in the primary school*, Schools Council

Research Studies, Macmillan, Basingstoke

Clough, E., Bailey, A., Bowley, R. and Coldron, J. (1985) 'Can topic work be assessed?' *Education 3–13*, vol. 13.1

Cohen, L., Thomas, J. and Manion, L. (1982) *Educational research and development in Britain 1970–1980*, NFER/Nelson, Windsor

Dearden, R. (1976) *Problems in primary education*, Routledge and Kegan Paul, London

De Bono, E. (1976) *Teaching thinking*, Temple Smith, New York

De Lacey, P.R. and Pryor, R.C. (1976) 'Senior high school pupils' aspirations for teaching and other professions', *South Pacific Journal of Teacher Education*, vol. 4.3, pp. 253–5

Department of Education and Science (1978) *Primary education in England*, HMSO, London

Dewey, J. (1910) *How we think*, Harrap, London

Eggleston, John (1980) 'The drawbacks of projects', *The Times Educational Supplement*, 12 September

Galton, M., Simon, B. and Croll, P. (1980a) *Inside the primary classroom*, Routledge and Kegan Paul, London

Galton, M., Simon, B. and Croll, P. (1980b) *Progress and performance in the primary classroom*, Routledge and Kegan Paul, London

Getzels, J. and Jackson, P. (1963) *Creativity and intelligence*, Wiley, New York

Goldman, R. (1964) *Religious thinking from childhood to adolescence*, Routledge and Kegan Paul, London

Goldman, R. (1966) *Readiness for religion*, Routledge and Kegan Paul, London

Gunning, S., Gunning, D. and Wilson, J. (1981) *Topic teaching in the primary school*, Croom Helm, London

Hellawell, D. and Smithers, A. (1973) 'Commitment to teaching of postgraduate and college-trained students', *Educational Research*, vol. 16.1, pp. 46–51

Henley, M. (1984) 'The findings of the 9–13 middle school survey: a local authority view', *Westminster Studies in Education*, vol.7, pp. 89–93

Hirst, P.H. (1974) *Knowledge and the curriculum*, Routledge and Kegan Paul, London

Holm, J. (1975) *Teaching religion in schools*, Oxford University Press, Oxford

House, E. (1980) *Evaluating with validity*, Sage Publications, California

Isaac, J. (1969) 'Social origins of trainee teachers', *Higher Education Journal*, vol. 17.3

Jeremiah, T.G. (1972) *A source book of creative themes*, Basil Blackwell, Oxford

Kenny, W. and Grotelveschen, A. (1984) 'Making the case for case study', *Journal of Curriculum Studies*, vol. 16.1, pp. 37–51

Kerry, T. (1982) 'Exceptional pupils in mixed ability classes and teachers' strategies for dealing with them', Unpublished PhD thesis, University of Nottingham

Kerry, T. (1984) 'Self report case-studies: an experiment in own classroom data collection by teachers', *Westminster Studies in Education*, vol. 7, pp. 103–11

Kilpatrick, W.H. (1918) 'The project method', *Teachers' College Record*, vol. 19, September

Kilpatrick, W.H. (1930) *Foundations of method*, Macmillan, New York

Knight, P. (1985) 'The practice of school-based curriculum development', *Journal of Curriculum Studies*, vol. 17.1, pp. 37–48

Krathwohl, D.R., Bloom, B.S. and Masia, B.B. (1964) *Taxonomy of Educational Objectives, Handbook II: Affective Domain*, McKay, New York

Lane, R. (1981) *Project work in the primary school*, Curriculum Development Centre, Preston

Luckmann, T. (1978) *Phenomenology and sociology*, Penguin, Harmondsworth

Miles, A. (1983) 'Developing pupils' thinking through topic work: a personally conducted case-study', BEd dissertation, University of Nottingham

Nisbet, J. and Watt, J. (1978) *Case study*, Rediguide 26, University of Nottingham

Ogilvy, E. (1973) *Gifted children in primary schools*, Macmillan, Basingstoke

Plowden Report (1967) *Children and their primary schools*, vol. 1, HMSO, London

Rance, P. (1968) *Teaching by topics*, Ward Lock, London

Reid, M. (1981) *Mixed ability teaching*, NFER, Windsor

Robbins Report (1963) *Report of the Robbins Committee on Higher Education*, HMSO, London

Rousseau, J.J. (1911) *Emile*, J.M. Dent, London

Rutter, M. *et al.* (1979) *Fifteen thousand hours*, Open Books, London

Sands, M. and Kerry, T. (1981) *Mixed ability teaching*, Croom Helm, London

Schools Council (1972) *Working paper 42: Education in the middle years*, Evans/Methuen, London

Schools Council (1973) *Integrated Studies Project*, Oxford University Press, Oxford

Simon, B. and Willcocks, J. (1981) *Research and practice in the primary classroom*, Routledge and Kegan Paul, London

Stake, R. and Day, J. (1978) in R. Stake and J. Easley (eds) *Case studies in science education*, Center for Instructional Research and Curriculum Development, Illinois

Stewart, J. (1986) *The making of the primary school*, Open University Press, Milton Keynes

Wragg, E.C. (1967) 'Attitudes, anxieties and aspirations of graduates following the PGCE', Unpublished MEd thesis, University of Leicester

Wragg, E.C. (1976) *Teaching mixed ability groups*, David and Charles, Newton Abbot

Wragg, E.C. (1978) 'A suitable case for imitation', *The Times Educational Supplement*

Wragg, E.C. (1983) *Classroom teaching skills*, Croom Helm, London

Wragg, E.C. and Kerry, T. (1978) *Classroom interaction research*, Rediguide 14, University of Nottingham

Resources

Success in topic work relies on a good choice of resources, which should include

- first-hand experiences for children;
- access to good books, good libraries and museum resources;
- effective visual aids, including posters, films, slides and television.

Below is a list of addresses from which high-quality visual material may be obtained.

Tecmedia Ltd, 5 Granby Street, Loughborough LE11 3LD (*Educational software: a creator's handbook*)

5–12, 2 Church Street, Seaford, Sussex BN25 1HD (Primary software specialists)

Artec Ltd, Salewheel House, Ribchester, Preston, Lancashire PR3 3XU (Save on Science catalogue)

Educational Foundation for Visual Aids, The George Building, Normal College, Bangor, Gwynedd LL57 2BZ

Trans-Ed Copying Services, 15 Ladybower Close, North Hykeham, Lincoln LN6 8EX

M R H Systems & Software, 20 Highfield Road, Kidderminster, Worcester DY10 2TL

London Urban Studies Service, c/o Notting Dale, Urban Studies Centre, 189 Freston Road, London W10 1YH

Council for Environmental Education, School of Education, University of Reading, London Road, Reading RG1 5AQ (environmental resource information)

Franklin Watts, 12A Golden Square, London W1R 4BA

Philip Green Educational Ltd, 112A Alcester Road, Studley, Warwickshire B80 7NR

For teachers, resources ought to include access to:
Child Education journal
Junior Education journal
Schools Council (1981–1983) Topic Work Resource Bank, School Curriculum Development Committee, Newcombe House, 45 Notting Hill Gate, London W11 3JB

These items listed all contain material of interest to teachers trying to improve their own skills, as well as indicating or containing material for direct classroom use.

Index